The Brazilian 43-tonne MBT Osorio.
▼

Armour 2000

Peter Gudgin

ARMS AND ARMOUR

First published in Great Britain in 1990 by Arms and Armour Press, Artillery House, Artillery Row, London SW1P 1RT.

Distributed in the USA by Sterling Publishing Co. Inc., 387 Park Avenue South, New York, NY 10016-8810.

Distributed in Australia by Capricorn Link (Australia) Pty. Ltd, P.O. Box 665, Lane Cove, New South Wales 2066, Australia.

British Library Cataloguing in Publication Data
Gudgin, Peter
Armour 2000.
1. Armour
I. Title
623
ISBN 1-85409-044-5

Jacket illustrations: Front, US Army troops in Germany leaving the Vilseck deprocessing area with their newly issued M1A1 Abrams tanks and heading for training exercises in Grafenwoehr. (Courtesy of General Dynamics Land Systems Division). Back, design graphic by Krauss Maffei. (Courtesy of Krauss Maffei Wehrtechnik GmbH)

Designed and edited by DAG Publications Ltd. Designed by David Gibbons; edited by Michael Boxall; layout by Anthony A. Evans; typeset by Typesetters (Birmingham) Ltd; camerawork by M&E Reproductions, North Fambridge, Essex; printed and bound in Great Britain by The Bath Press, Avon.

▶
The latest US MBT, M1A1 Abrams. (General Dynamics Land Systems Division)

CONTENTS

Acknowledgements

It would be a very knowledgeable person indeed who could write a book such as this without outside help, and I gratefully acknowledge the help given to me by the majority of the armoured fighting vehicle manufacturers of the Western world, in providing views and opinions on future AFV development, data on and photographs of their current products and permission to reproduce these photographs here.

I am especially grateful to Dr Cyril Watson, Director and Chief Engineer, and Mr Fred Garner, Weapon Systems Manager, of GKN Defence; Brigadier Arthur Gooch commanding the Royal Armoured Corps Centre at Bovington; the Public Information Branches at HQ British Army of the Rhine and 1(BR) Corps; Dott. Attilio di Giovanni, Director of S.p.A. Oto Melara, La Spezia, Italy; and Judith Ferraro of General Dynamics Land Systems Division, Warren, Michigan, USA, for the additional help which they have given me.

Grateful acknowledgement is also due to George Forty and his staff at the Bovington Tank Museum for permission to publish some of the photographs from their extensive archive; the British MoD; the US Army Tank and Automotive Command; the US Army Intelligence and Threat Analysis Center for information on certain Soviet AFVs; and the Defence Attaché's staff at the US Embassy in London for pointing me in the right direction when I was seeking information.

Peter Gudgin
LEAMINGTON SPA, MARCH 1989

When the year 2000 arrives, more than 80 years will have passed since the first tracked armoured fighting vehicle, or tank, was introduced into service in 1916 by the British Army, in an effort to break the stalemate imposed on the Western Front by the machine-gun, barbed wire entanglements and the defensive line of trenches which stretched from the North Sea coast of Belgium in the north to the Swiss frontier in the south. Some means of breaking through the enemy's lines and reintroducing mobility to the battlefield without incurring the crippling casualties which the machine-gun and the artillery barrage inflicted was essential if victory was ever to be won, and it was in desperation that the War Office turned its attention back to various proposals, previously rejected, for bullet-proof self-propelled vehicles with trench-crossing and cross-country ability, which had been made from 1900 onwards.

The idea of an armoured fighting vehicle is almost as old as the wheel; the armoured war chariot was known in 2000 BC, and armoured war carts were used in the 15th and 16th centuries. Leonardo da Vinci proposed such a vehicle in 1482, when he wrote: 'I am building secure and covered chariots which are invulnerable, and when they advance with their guns into the midst of the foe even the largest enemy masses must retire and behind these chariots the infantry can follow in safety.' The problem with these proposals, however, was that they relied for motive power either upon the horse or upon the vehicle crew; the limitations of these power sources meant that permissible vehicle weight, and thus protection, was limited to that which could be towed by the horse or propelled by the crew. A further weight limitation was imposed by the capacity of the ground over which the vehicle was moving to support the pressure exerted on it by the vehicle's narrow wheels; too great a ground pressure meant that the vehicle sank up to its axles and became immobile.

It was not until the middle of the 19th century that the limitation of inadequate motive power began to be lifted, with the invention of the steam engine; steam-powered artillery tractors with improved cross-country mobility were used in the Crimean War by the British Army, but even this power source could not produce a high enough ratio of power to weight to give adequate mobility to a fighting vehicle carrying sufficient protection as well as firepower. The armoured fighting vehicle did not become a viable proposition until the invention of the internal combustion engine, and the first such

vehicles, mounting a machine-gun with an armoured shield on a wheeled rather than tracked chassis, were designed in 1898 by an Englishman, Frederick R. Simms, and an American, Colonel R. P. Davidson. Similar vehicles were later produced in Germany, Italy, Belgium and France, and the first use of armoured cars, as they came to be called, in a campaign was by the Italians in their Libyan campaign against the Turks in 1911–12.

The use of wheels meant that the vehicles were confined, for all practical purposes, to use on roads; armoured versions of civilian cars, armed with machine-guns, were used for offensive road patrols in Belgium by both the Belgians and the British Royal Naval Air Service in the early days of the First World War, but once the stalemate of trench warfare had set in, their lack of cross-country mobility meant that their use was restricted to roads in rear areas. They were little used after the winter of 1914/15.

Another break-through was required before the armoured fighting vehicle could begin to play its part in bringing mobility back to the battlefield; some means had to be found, not only of crossing soft and uneven ground but also of crossing trenches and cutting through complicated barbed-wire entanglements. There are several conflicting claims as to who, and in which country, first suggested the idea of what ultimately became known as the tank; the concept itself is lost in the mists of time, and there is no doubt that similar proposals were submitted at about the same time in several countries. Certainly official trials were started in early 1915 quite independently in both France and the United Kingdom, those in the UK being conducted under the aegis of the Admiralty as a logical development of the RNAS armoured cars whose use in Flanders had been so drastically curtailed by the introduction of trench warfare and the artillery bombardment. There is no doubt, however, that the British were first in the field with a viable tank and the first to employ it in action, in September 1916.

Two possible lines of approach to the problem of crossing both soft ground and trenches presented themselves – the 'big wheel' and the linked track. The wheel needed to be of sufficiently large diameter both to lower the vehicle ground pressure to an acceptable figure and to span the average trench width of ten feet; this meant that a diameter of at least fifteen feet was required, which in turn meant a large, unwieldy and vulnerable vehicle. After building a mockup of such a vehicle, the British rejected the 'big wheel' in favour of a tracked solution; a similar conclusion was reached by the French, after trials of a prototype tractor fitted with large-diameter wheels. The Holt Caterpillar tractor was chosen by the French, and later by the Germans, as the basis for their tracked armoured fighting vehicle; although Holt tractors were in service as artillery prime movers in the British Army, none could be spared for experiments with landships, as the Admiralty vehicles were known, so that other types of commercially available track had to be used. None of these gave the required performance, and an entirely new track had to be specially designed for the purpose.

The first British General Staff specification for the tracked fighting vehicle was issued in June 1915, and required a trench-crossing ability of ten feet and a vertical step-climbing capacity of four feet six inches. The first prototype vehicle designed to meet these requirements was designed and built in six weeks by the Lincoln firm of Foster, and was known as the 'No. 1 Lincoln Machine'; it failed to meet them in its trials in September 1915, but showed sufficient promise for development to be continued, and the modified prototype, known as 'Little Willie', also underwent its trial in September 1915 with improved cross-country performance but still inadequate step-climbing ability. The design of both prototypes bore a remarkable resemblance to the tanks of the inter-war years in that they were designed to carry a gun mounted in a turret giving 360 degrees of traverse and both were carried on 'half-round tracks'; their failure to meet the stated requirement was due more to the extraordinary nature of the requirement than to any shortcoming in basic design, the soundness of which is proved by the fact that the majority of current battle tanks are logical developments of it.

Meanwhile, another design was being developed. It had become obvious that to increase the vertical step-climbing and trench-crossing performance it was necessary to increase both the length of track on the ground and the height of the front track wheel above the ground; calculations had also shown that, to meet the cross-country and trench-crossing requirement, the 'big wheel' machine would have needed a wheel with a diameter of sixty feet. The new machine was therefore designed so that the track on the ground conformed to the curve of a wheel of this size and so that the front track 'horns' were both some five feet above the ground and projecting well forward of the

tank hull, to give the track an unimpeded approach to any obstacle. These two design parameters ensured that the new tank design, known as 'Big Willie' or 'Mother', would perform better across country than either the French or German heavy tanks produced during the First World War. The design of 'Mother' was begun in August 1915 and the prototype moved under its own power, and fired its guns, in January 1916. Successful in its trials, it went into production as the Tank Mark I in February 1916 and its basic design remained largely unchanged through Marks I to V and a total UK production of 2,222 vehicles; its characteristic lozenge shape and its side sponsons carrying the armament are perpetuated in the cap and collar badges and the cloth arm badge of the British Royal Tank Regiment.

The maximum designed speed of the heavy tank was four miles per hour, infantry marching speed; across shell-torn country, however, its maximum speed was considerably reduced. The prospect of the breakthrough for which they had been designed being achieved by the heavy tanks raised the probability of open warfare on good firm ground, and such warfare would require a lighter, faster tank to exploit the opportunities created by the breakthrough and to co-operate with mounted troops. This tank, known as the Medium or Whippet, was designed in December 1916 and bore a resemblance to 'Little Willie' in that it had half-round tracks and the engine superstructure and turret projected above the top run of the track. It went into production as the Medium Mark A in 1917 and was first in action in March 1918. Of the four Marks of Medium designed and built during the First World War, only the Mark A saw action; it had a crew of three, while the Marks B, C and D had four-man crews. All except the Mark D had top speeds of between six and eight miles per hour; the Mark D was a giant leap forward with a maximum of twenty-five miles per hour.

As already stated, the heavy tank had been designed to meet a specific and very unusual requirement, the crossing of deep, wide trenches, with the ability to fire its guns, from both sides simultaneously, down the length of the trenches being crossed; this was the reason for the mounting of the armament in side sponsons rather than in a traversing turret. When the reason for its introduction disappeared with the end of the First World War, so did this design of tank, leaving the Medium design to be developed into the main battle tanks of today.

Although the First World War lozenge design of heavy tank was phased out, the idea of having a heavily armoured, slow tank to accompany the infantry and a faster, lighter tank to exploit the breakthrough was retained in the armies of most countries after the war; in fact, a third category of lightly armed and armoured light tanks was added to these two between the wars, partly as a means of training armoured troops in the tactical use of armour more cheaply than would have been the case with heavy and medium tanks, and partly for use in campaigns in difficult country such as the NW frontier of India, against lightly armed rebel guerrillas. In the British Army, the slow, heavily armoured tank was known as the Infantry or 'I' Tank and the faster, more lightly armoured vehicle as the Cruiser Tank. The general design of light, medium and heavy tanks conformed to that of 'Little Willie' in having half-round tracks, a rear engine compartment, a central fighting compartment carrying a turret with 360° traverse mounting the main armament, and a driver's compartment in the front. Various designs of tank with auxiliary machine-gun turrets in addition to the main turret were tried in various countries during the inter-war period, but these were gradually abandoned as wasteful of weight and manpower, and tank design settled down to the basic layout described above during the Second World War. In the heavy tank category, primary consideration was given to protection, with firepower in second place and mobility very much last; for medium and light tanks, mobility came first, with firepower again in second place and protection last.

In addition to the three main categories of tank, the inventories of most armies continued to contain wheeled armoured cars, varying from armoured versions of civilian vehicles, armed with one or more machine-guns, to purpose-designed wheeled armoured vehicles with enhanced cross-country mobility stemming from multi-wheeled drive, lockable differentials, tyres capable of functioning when punctured, specially designed suspension systems capable of large wheel movement and with a gun rather than a machine-gun as main armament. These were required to have high road speeds, and were used for reconnaissance and high-speed exploitation of unexpected breakthroughs, as well as support of the Civil Power in peacetime, where their relative quietness of operation and greater capacity for fast movement over large distances was an advantage.

As in the First World War, many variants of the basic tracked vehicle were also developed for special purposes during the Second World War; tracked infantry and load-carriers, recovery vehicles, self-propelled artillery carriers, bulldozers, crane, command and bridging vehicles and many others were all introduced in order that the tanks could be adequately supported, while other tracked special devices were devised for the clearance of mines, amphibious landings and the penetration of defences such as the Siegfried Line and the Atlantic Wall. It was as a result of experience gained in North Africa, Italy, north-west Europe and the Soviet Union during the Second World War that tank design firmed up in its present form; the earlier requirement for different types of tank for different tasks was seen to be wasteful of resources, as one tank of suitable design and performance could carry out adequately all the tasks previously carried out by medium, heavy, Infantry and Cruiser tanks. The need for machine-guns additional to those in the turret was similarly seen to be wasteful of manpower, although the majority of British, American, Soviet and German tanks carried a hull-mounted machine-gun beside the driver throughout the war.

The lessons in tank design learned by the various combatant countries during the war depended very much on their experiences in combat; the German Army found itself outnumbered and outmanoeuvred by the faster US Sherman and Soviet T-34 tanks, and therefore placed mobility together with firepower at the top of its priority list for the characteristics of its post-war tanks in 1956. The British Royal Armoured Corps, whose tanks had been consistently out-gunned by those of its German opponents throughout the war, naturally placed firepower and protection at the top of its list of requirements, with mobility very much in third place. The Soviet Army, which had got its wartime tank design just about right with the T-34 medium and KV heavy tanks, found its judgement justified and continued after the war with more of the same. That the correct answer to the armoured fighting vehicle requirement has been found would appear to be confirmed by the remarkable similarity in basic layout and even external appearance between the present main battle tanks of West Germany (Leopard 1 and 2), the UK (Chieftain and Challenger), France (Leclerc), Italy (OF-40 and C-1) and the USA (M-1); only the USSR, of the major tank-producing powers, differs, preferring to persist with lighter tanks of lower silhouette, with firepower ahead of mobility as their most important characteristic and protection very much the lowest priority.

For reconnaissance, most armies have persisted with wheeled armoured vehicles since the Second World War; only Britain has perversely re-introduced a tracked light tank for this purpose when seeking to replace its highly successful Saladin armoured car in the 1960s. In fact it chose the worst of both worlds by opting for both a wheeled armoured car (CVR (W)) and a tracked light tank (CVR(T)) for the reconnaissance role, in deference to the two factions in the Royal Armoured Corps whose views on the subject were quite irreconcilable; as a result, it is still paying the financial, training and logistic penalty and neither of the chosen replacements performs as well as the vehicle it replaced. In the selection of a light tank to fill part of the reconnaissance role, the British Army has repeated the mistake it made before the war with its Light Tank series; it is inadequately armed and protected to be able to fulfil a useful role on the modern battlefield, and will therefore have to be relegated to the tactical training role in wartime. Equally, a tracked armoured vehicle is too aggressive in appearance and arouses too much emotion for it to be usable in support of the civil power, whereas wheeled armoured cars are acceptable in this role.

Experience in two world wars has shown that, whereas the tank can take ground, it cannot hold it alone; infantry is required for this purpose, and, if infantry is to accompany the tanks, it must have a vehicle to enable it to do so which can keep up with the tanks and which will give reasonable protection to the infantrymen it is carrying, as well as having firepower for its own defence. Such vehicles are known as infantry combat vehicles (ICVs), and they are specially designed tracked armoured vehicles with a cross-country performance close to that of the tank. For the transport of infantry up to the battle zone, rather than within it, and where a limited amount of cross-country mobility and armoured protection will suffice, armoured personnel carriers (APCs), which may be wheeled or tracked, are employed; many types of APC were employed by the British, US and German Armies during the war and some, by the British, in the First World War, but the Infantry Combat Vehicle is a post-1945 introduction, the concept of which is as yet untried in action.

Today, most countries appear to have agreed on the optimum shape, size and weight of the tank, which must, in any event, be a compromise between the basic characteristics of firepower, mobility and protection; improvements and developments are only of detail, such as miniaturization of target acquisition and fire control systems, improved means of protection, improved armament and ammunition, and improvements in mobility allied to new suspension systems and more powerful power plants, rather than in the basic design of the vehicle. For example, improved means of target acquisition and engagement have put the US M-1 and the German Leopard 2 tanks so far ahead of the British Chieftain and Challenger in the annual NATO Canadian Trophy tank shooting competition that the British Royal Armoured Corps has withdrawn from the competition to save itself from further embarrassment. Furthermore, as a result of the recent improvements in ammunition and ballistics of smooth bore guns, the majority of the major tank-producing powers have opted for smooth bore guns as the main armament of their main battle tanks; only the British Army remains wedded to the rifled gun, with its limitations on the use of 'fire and forget' projectiles and its other disadvantages, which will be discussed in more detail later in the book.

For a weapon which, on its introduction in 1916, was thought to be of only limited use and likely to have a short life, the tank has been an unconscionable time a-dying; it will certainly continue well into the 21st century in the service of the armies of the world. However, its vulnerability to newly emerging weapons and methods of attack, together with its present very high, and rapidly increasing, cost are likely to have an increasingly limiting effect on its usefulness and availability in the years ahead, at least in its present form; the problem of providing mobile firepower with adequate protection for its crew could well find other, cheaper and less vulnerable solutions than the tank in the future. Limitations on defence budgets are likely to place constraints on the acquisition of future tank fleets in most Western countries, and these are likely to lead to a requirement for tanks of the next generation to be lighter, smaller and with a smaller crew than the present 60-tonne monsters; to reduce money spent on training their crews, these tanks will also be required to be simpler to operate and to maintain than those at present in service.

Of the multitude of AFVs in service with the armies of the world today, few are likely still to be in service in the year 2000, at least in the front-line armies of the First World. Many will still be in service in Third World armies, however, having been cast off and sold by the NATO and Warsaw Pact countries as they have become outdated and obsolescent. Only the former are covered in this book, and are described and illustrated in the outline specifications forming Part I; the latter are not of sufficient note to merit their inclusion in a book dealing with armour in the 21st century and are, in any event, fully described and illustrated elsewhere. The Bibliography lists suitable sources.

In Part II, possible future lines of development of the AFV are discussed, under the headings of the major armoured vehicle characteristics of Firepower, Mobility and Protection; a further chapter is devoted to General Design, in which the advantages and disadvantages of possible future developments are discussed in relation to the vehicle as a whole, together with their effect on performance and other design aspects and characteristics of the fighting vehicle.

List of Abbreviations and Acronyms

AA Anti-Aircraft
AAMG Anti-Aircraft Machine-Gun
AFV Armoured Fighting Vehicle
AP Armour-Piercing
APC (i) Armoured Personnel Carrier; (ii) Armour Piercing, Capped
APCBC Armour-Piercing, Capped, Ballistic Cap
AP/CR Armour-Piercing/ Composite Rigid
APDS Armour-Piercing Discarding Sabot
APFSDS Armour-Piercing Fin-Stabilized Discarding Sabot
ARV Armoured Recovery Vehicle
AVLB Armoured Vehicle-Launched Bridge
AVRE Armoured Vehicle Royal Engineers
BARV Beach Armoured Recovery Vehicle
bhp Brake Horse Power
BMP *Borevaya Mashina Pyekhota* (Infantry Fighting Vehicle)
BRDM *Bronirovannaya*

Razdivatelnaya Dozornaya Mashina (Armoured Scout Patrol Vehicle)
BT *Bystriy Tankov* (Fast Tank)
BTR *Bronetransporter* (Armoured Transporter)
BW Bacteriological Warfare
CDL Canal Defence Light
CE Chemical Energy
CET Combat Engineer Tractor
CO₂ Carbon Dioxide
CVR(T) Combat Vehicle, Reconnaissance (Tracked)
CVR(W) Combat Vehicle, Reconnaissance (Wheeled)
CW Chemical Warfare
DERV Diesel-Engined Road Vehicle (Diesel Fuel)
EMP Electro-Magnetic Pulse
FLIR Forward-Looking Infra-Red
FRG Federal Republic of Germany
FSDS Fin-Stabilized Discarding Sabot
GW Guided Weapon
HAN Hydroxyl Ammonium Nitrate
HE High-Explosive

HEAT High-Explosive Anti-Tank
HEP High-Explosive Plastic
HESH High-Explosive Squash Head
hp Horse Power
I Tank Infantry Tank
ICV Infantry Combat Vehicle
IFV Infantry Fighting Vehicle
II Image Intensifier
in Inch(es)
IR Infra-Red
IS Josef Stalin
KE Kinetic Energy
km Kilometre
kN Kilonewton
KT Kiloton
KV Klimenti Voroshilov
kW Kilowatt
LASER Light Amplification by Stimulated Emission of Radiation
lb Pounds weight
L/C Steering Ratio (Length of track on ground/width between track Centres)
LLTV Low Light Level Television
LP Liquid Propellant

m Metre(s)
MBT Main Battle Tank
MG Machine-Gun
MICV Mechanized Infantry Combat Vehicle
MLC Military Load Capacity
mph Miles Per Hour
MV Muzzle Velocity
NATO North Atlantic Treaty Organization
NBC Nuclear, Biological, Chemical
Nd YAG Neodymium Glass
NGP Nominal Ground Pressure
NIH Not Invented Here
NOTE Nap Of The Earth
Pz Beob Wg Armoured OP Vehicle
Pz Berge Wg Armoured Recovery Vehicle
Pz Kpfw Tank
RARDE Royal Armament Research and Development Establishment
SADE Specialized Armour Development Establishment
SDI Strategic Defense Initiative
SP Self-Propelled
TI Thermal Imaging

Tracked vehicles

Main battle tanks The Main Battle Tank of today is, as its name implies, the main tank in an army's equipment inventory, the tank with which it will fight its main battles. Until the end of the Second World War, most armies had several categories of tank, such as infantry and cruiser, or light, medium and heavy, distinguished by weight category or function; by the end of the war, however, it was realized that just one tank, suitably armed, mobile and protected, could perfectly well perform all the functions formerly carried out by the various categories previously thought necessary, with consequent production, logistic and cost benefits.

The first true MBT was the British Centurion, introduced in 1945 in answer to Field Marshal Montgomery's call for a universal tank; a medium weight compromise was aimed at, between the 68 tonnes of the German Pz Kpfw Tiger Model B (Royal Tiger) and the 30 or so tonnes of the average medium tank, and the Centurion in its original form weighed some 45 tonnes. Since then, the weights of MBTs have crept remorselessly upwards, until the Challenger, Leopard 2 and Abrams, typical of the genre, now weigh in at some 60 tonnes or more. This is obviously too heavy for adequate mobility, either strategic or tactical, and the generation after next will probably be both smaller and lighter. One way ahead is being pointed by the Brazilian company Engesa, with its 43-tonne MBT Osorio; others may lie in the direction of turretless tanks, with externally mounted guns and a three-man crew carried in the hull.

Of the many MBTs in the service of the armies of the world today, those listed in the following pages are those most likely still to be in first-line service with First World armies after the year 2000. Those of the NATO armies have an external resemblance to one another, thanks to the slab-sided look of hull and turret encased in composite armour, the skirting plates over the running gear and the large diameter road wheels. Similarly, it will be noticed that the Warsaw Pact tanks also have a family resemblance to one another, although very different from those of the NATO countries, arising out of their low, rounded turret silhouette, low overall height and very long guns.

The Engesa Osorio is included, as it represents a first attempt to bring the weight of the MBT down to a reasonable figure while retaining the firepower, mobility and much of the protection of modern MBTs.

Main Battle Tank: Brazil	
Osorio	
Weight in action	43 tonnes
Crew	4
Overall length (gun front)	10.1m
Overall width	3.26m
Overall height	2.89m
Ground clearance	0.46m
Length of track on ground	4.49m
Track width	0.57m
Main armament:	
calibre	120mm, smooth
length in calibres	not available
stabilized (traverse/elevation)	yes
number of rounds carried	38
Auxiliary armament	7.62mm coaxial MG
Power plant	MWM V-12 4-stroke diesel
Max. output	1,040bhp
Power/weight ratio	24.2hp/tonne
Suspension	hydro-pneumatic
Nominal ground pressure	82.4kN/m^2
Performance:	
max. speed (roads)	70km/hr
range (roads)	550km
fording depth	2m (with preparation)

Main Battle Tank: France
Leclerc

Weight in action	53 tonnes
Crew	3
Overall length (gun front)	9.6m
Overall width	3.67m
Overall height	2.3m
Ground clearance	0.5m
Length of track on ground	4.3m
Track width	0.635m
Main armament:	
calibre	120mm, smooth
length in calibres	52
stabilized (traverse/elevation)	yes
number of rounds carried	40, auto-loaded
Power plant	UniDiesel V-8 turbo-charged
Max. output	1,500bhp
Power/weight ratio	30bhp/tonne
Suspension	torsion bar or hydro-gas
Nominal ground pressure	$9N/cm^2$
Performance:	
max. speed (roads)	70km/hr
range (roads)	550km
fording depth	4m (with preparation)

Main Battle Tank: Federal Germany
Leopard 2

Weight in action	55 tonnes
Crew	4
Overall length (gun front)	9.668m
Overall width	3.7m
Overall height	2.79m
Ground clearance	0.48m
Length of track on ground	5.245m
Track width	0.635m
Main armament:	
calibre	120mm, smooth
length in calibres	not available
stabilized (traverse/elevation)	yes
number of rounds carried	42
Auxiliary armament	7.62mm coaxial MG
Power plant	MTU MB 873 12-cyl multi-fuel
Max. output	1,500bhp
Power/weight ratio	27bhp/tonne
Suspension	torsion bar
Nominal ground pressure	11.5psi
	$(0.81kg/cm^2)$
Performance:	
max. speed (roads)	72km/hr
range (roads)	550km
fording depth	4m (with snorkel

Main Battle Tank: Israel
Merkava Mk 2

Weight in action	60 tonnes
Crew	4
Overall length (gun front)	8.63m
Overall width	3.7m
Overall height	2.75m
Ground clearance	0.53m
Length of track on ground	4.52m
Track width	0.64m
Main armament:	
calibre	105mm
length in calibres	50.9
stabilized (traverse/elevation)	yes, electro-hydraulic
number of rounds carried	62
Auxiliary armament	7.62mm MG & 60mm mortar
Power plant	Teledyne V-12 4-stroke diesel
Max. output	908bhp
Power/weight ratio	15bhp/tonne
Suspension	independent, coil spring
Performance:	
max. speed (roads)	58km/hr
range (roads)	500km
fording depth	2m (with preparation)

Main Battle Tank: Italy
Ariete (C1)

Weight in action	50 tonnes
Crew	4
Overall length (gun front)	10.54m
Overall width	3.7m
Overall height	2.46m
Track width	0.618m
Main armament:	
calibre	120mm, smooth
length in calibres	44
stabilized (traverse/elevation)	yes
Auxiliary armament	7.62mm coaxial MG
Power plant	FIAT V-12 diesel
Max. output	1,200bhp
Power/weight ratio	24bhp/tonne
Suspension	torsion bar
Nominal ground pressure	12psi (0.85kg/cm^2)
Performance:	
max. speed (roads)	65km/hr
range (roads)	550km
fording depth	4m (with preparation)

Main Battle Tank: Japan
TK-X (Type 90?)

Weight in action	50 tonnes
Crew	3
Overall length (gun front)	9.7m
Overall width	3.4m
Overall height	2.3m
Ground clearance	variable, 0.2–0.6m
Main armament:	
calibre	120mm, smooth
length in calibres	not available
stabilized (traverse/elevation)	yes
number of rounds carried	?, auto-loaded
Auxiliary armament	7.62mm coaxial MG
Power plant	Mitsubishi 10-cyl diesel
Max. output	1,500bhp
Power/weight ratio	30bhp/tonne
Suspension	hydro-gas & torsion bar
Performance:	
max. speed (roads)	70km/hr
range (roads)	300km
fording depth	2m

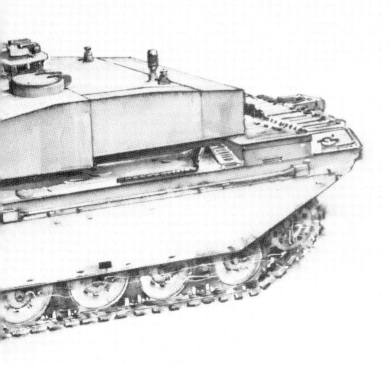

Main Battle Tank: South Korea
K-1 (Tank 88)

Weight in action	51 tonnes
Crew	4
Overall length (gun front)	9.7m
Overall width	3.6m
Overall height	2.3m
Ground clearance	0.46m
Main armament:	
calibre	105mm
length in calibres	50.9
stabilized (traverse/elevation)	yes
number of rounds carried	47
Auxiliary armament	7.62mm coaxial MG
Power plant	MTU diesel MB 871Ka
Max. output	1,200bhp
Power/weight ratio	23.5bhp/tonne
Suspension	hydro-gas & torsion bar
Nominal ground pressure	12psi (0.86kg/cm²)

Performance:	
max. speed (roads)	65km/hr
range (roads)	500km
fording depth	2m (with preparation)

Main Battle Tank: UK
Challenger 2

This vehicle is the Vickers Defence Systems' proposal to meet the British Army requirement for a replacement for their Chieftain fleet. Prototypes will be available for trial in early 1990, and will then be tested in competition with the US M1A1 Abrams to select which vehicle best meets the British Army requirements. Deliveries to the British Army of the chosen replacement are scheduled to start in 1992.

Challenger 2 differs from Challenger 1 mainly in the turret and particularly in the target acquisition and fire control system, although retaining the thermal imaging system of the earlier version. Its overall dimensions and performance are similar.

It will mount the improved (but rifled) 120mm L30 high-pressure gun developed by the Royal Armament Research & Development Establishment, which will later be retro-fitted to the British Challenger 1 fleet.

(For Challenger 1, see overleaf.)

Main Battle Tank: UK
Challenger 1

Weight in action	60 tonnes
Crew	4
Overall length (gun front)	11.55m
Overall width	3.51m
Overall height	2.89m
Ground clearance	0.5m
Track width	0.65m
Main armament:	
calibre	120mm, rifled
length in calibres	55
stabilized (traverse/elevation)	yes
number of rounds carried	48–52
Auxiliary armament	7.62mm coaxial MG
Power plant	Rolls-Royce V-12 Condor diesel
Max. output	1,200bhp
Power/weight ratio	20bhp/tonne
Suspension	hydro-gas
Nominal ground pressure	13.6psi (0.96kg/cm^2)
Performance:	
max. speed (roads)	70km/hr
fording depth	1.07m

Main Battle Tank: USA
M1A1 Abrams

Weight in action	59 tonnes
Crew	4
Overall length (gun front)	9.8m
Overall width	3.65m
Overall height	2.44m
Ground clearance	0.48m
Length of track on ground	4.65m
Track width	0.635m
Main armament:	
calibre	120mm, smooth
length in calibres	not available
stabilized (traverse/elevation)	yes
number of rounds carried	55
Auxiliary armament	7.62mm coaxial MG
Power plant	Avco AGT1500 gas turbine
Max. output	1,500bhp
Power/weight ratio	25bhp/tonne
Suspension	torsion bar
Nominal ground pressure	13.7psi (0.96kg/cm^2)

Performance:

max. speed (roads)	67km/hr
range (roads)	450km
fording depth	2m (with preparation)

Main Battle Tank: USSR
T-64

Weight in action	38 tonnes
Crew	3
Overall length (gun front)	9.1m
Overall width	3.4m
Overall height	2.3m
Ground clearance	0.43m
Length of track on ground	4.1m
Track width	0.58m
Main armament:	
calibre	125mm, smooth
length in calibres	48
stabilized (traverse/elevation)	yes
number of rounds carried	40, auto-loaded
Auxiliary armament	7.62mm coaxial MG
Power plant	5-cyl opposed piston diesel
Max. output	750bhp
Power/weight ratio	20bhp/tonne
Suspension	torsion bar
Nominal ground pressure	11psi (0.77kg/cm^2)

Performance:

max. speed (roads)	60km/hr
range (roads) on internal tanks	450km
fording depth	5.5m (with snorkel)

Main Battle Tank: USSR
T-72

Weight in action	41 tonnes
Crew	3
Overall length (gun front)	9.53m
Overall width	3.46m
Overall height	2.39m
Ground clearance	0.43m
Length of track on ground	4.25m
Track width	0.58m
Main armament:	
calibre	125mm, smooth
length in calibres	48
stabilized (traverse/elevation)	yes
number of rounds carried	39, auto-loaded
Auxiliary armament	7.62mm coaxial MG
Power plant	V-46 12-cyl Vee, diesel
Max. output	780bhp
Power/weight ratio	19bhp/tonne
Suspension	torsion bar
Nominal ground pressure	12psi (0.83kg/cm^2)

Performance:
max. speed (roads)	60km/hr
range (roads) on internal tanks	450km
fording depth	5.5m (with snorkel)

Main Battle Tank: USSR
T-80

Weight in action	42 tonnes
Crew	3
Overall length (gun front)	9.2m
Overall width	3.6m
Overall height	2.3m
Ground clearance	0.43m
Track width	0.58m
Main armament:	
calibre	125mm, smooth
length in calibres	48
stabilized (traverse/elevation)	yes
number of rounds carried	40, auto-loaded
Auxiliary armament	7.62mm coaxial MG
Power plant	gas turbine
Max. output	900bhp
Power/weight ratio	21bhp/tonne
Suspension	hydro-gas?
Nominal ground pressure	12psi (0.85kg/cm^2)

Performance:
max. speed (roads)	70km/hr
range (roads) on internal tanks	450km
fording depth	5.5m (with snorkel)

Infantry combat vehicles and armoured personnel carriers The use of armoured tracked vehicles for the transport of infantry on and to the battlefield dates back to the First World War; early in 1918 the British produced a version of their heavy tank Mark V, modified for the carriage of infantry, with sliding doors in place of the gun sponsons, and followed it up with the purpose-designed supply tank Mark IX, which could carry 30 troops in addition to the crew, later that year.

With the increase in mobility and protection of the main battle tank in the past two decades, the need has arisen for a tracked vehicle for the carriage of supporting infantry which has mobility and protection equivalent to that of the MBT and which has, in addition, sufficient firepower of its own to be able to take on and knock out enemy infantry carriers. After much heart-searching in the armies of NATO, and much cap-badge politics in the British Army in particular, this need has eventually been recognized, and

a series of infantry fighting vehicles has resulted which is currently entering service; these are the British Warrior, the US Bradley and the Italian Puma. The FRG Marder has been in service now for some years, while the French equivalent, the AMX 10P, is now somewhat out of date, under-armed and under-protected.

The tracked APCs of the NATO armies, such as the British FV432 and the US M-113 are all due for replacement and unlikely to survive into the 21st century except as cast-offs sold to the armies of the Third World; as they consist of nothing more than lightly armoured boxes on tracks, with low power/weight ratios and poor cross-country mobility, they are omitted from the list of current vehicles with potential.

IFV/APC: UK

Warrior

Weight in action	24 tonnes
Crew	2
Personnel capacity	10
Overall length	5.4m
Overall width	2.8m
Overall height	2.8m
Ground clearance	0.5m
Length of track on ground	3.8m
Track width	0.46m
Main armament:	
calibre	30mm
stabilized (traverse/elevation)	no
number of rounds carried	176
Auxiliary armament	7.62mm chain gun
Power plant	Rolls-Royce V-8 diesel
Max. output	550bhp
Power/weight ratio	23.5bhp/tonne
Suspension	transverse torsion bar w/rotary dampers
Nominal ground pressure	10.8psi (8kg/cm^2)
Performance:	
max. speed (roads)	80km/hr
range (roads)	500km
fording depth	1.3m

IFV/APC: Federal Germany
Marder

Weight in action	28.2 tonnes
Crew	4
Personnel capacity	6
Overall length	6.8m
Overall width	3.2m
Overall height	2.9m
Ground clearance	0.45m
Length of track on ground	3.9m
Track width	0.45m
Main armament:	
calibre	20mm
stabilized (traverse/elevation)	no
number of rounds carried	1,250
Auxiliary armament	7.62mm coaxial MG
Power plant	MTU MB 833 6-cyl diesel
Max. output	600bhp
Power/weight ratio	21bhp/tonne
Suspension	transverse torsion bar
Nominal ground pressure	12psi (0.8kg/cm^2)
Performance:	
max. speed (roads)	75km/hr
range (roads)	520km
fording depth	2.5m (with preparation)

IFV/APC: USA
M-2 Bradley

Weight in action	22.7 tonnes
Crew	3
Personnel capacity	7
Overall length	6.2m
Overall width	3.2m
Overall height	2.9m
Ground clearance	0.46m
Length of track on ground	3.9m
Track width	0.53m
Main armament:	
calibre	25mm chain gun
stabilized (traverse/elevation)	yes
number of rounds carried	900
Auxiliary armament	2-rd TOW GW launcher
	7.62mm coaxial MG
Power plant	Cummins 8-cyl diesel
Max. output	500bhp'
Power/weight ratio	22bhp/tonne
Suspension	transverse torsion bar
Nominal ground pressure	7.7psi (0.54kg/cm^2)
Performance:	
max. speed (roads)	66km/hr
range (roads)	480km
fording depth	amphibious

IFV/APC: USSR **BMP-2**					
Weight in action	15 tonnes	Length of track on ground	3.5m	Max. output	300bhp
Crew	2	Track width	0.3m	Power/weight ratio	20bhp/tonne
Personnel capacity	8	Main armament:		Suspension	transverse torsion bar
Overall length	6.8m	calibre	30mm	Nominal ground pressure	
Overall width	3.4m	stabilized (traverse/elevation)	no		8.5psi (0.6kg/cm^2)
Overall height	2.1m	number of rounds carried	250	Performance:	
Ground clearance	0.4m	Auxiliary armament	AT-5 Spandrel ATGW	max. speed (roads)	80km/hr
			7.62mm coaxial MG	range (roads)	500km
		Power plant	UTD-20 6-cyl diesel	fording depth	amphibious

Reconnaissance vehicles Nowhere has the argument between proponents of wheeled and tracked vehicles waged more strongly and more indecisively than in the field of reconnaissance. Reconnaissance in most armies had been a cavalry function, and cavalrymen did not take kindly to mechanization when it came; if they had to give up their horses, they preferred the lesser of the two mechanical evils and opted therefore for the quieter, faster (at that time) and easier to maintain wheeled vehicle, rather than the dirty, noisy and (relatively) slow tracked equivalent. The more mechanically-minded tank men, on the other hand, preferred the challenge presented by the tracked vehicle, together with its superior, 'go anywhere' cross-country performance.

These prejudices have continued down the years and still exist today, with the result that the US Army, for example, has had no wheeled reconnaissance vehicle since the Second World War. The West German Army, on the other hand, has preferred wheels for reconnaissance both during and since the war. The Russian, French and British Armies have sat on the fence and have given themselves a logistic and training headache as a result by having both wheeled and tracked recce

vehicles in service at the same time; indeed, Britain, with the CVR (W) and (T), and France, with the AMX10 and 10P, introduced new wheeled and tracked reconnaissance vehicles into service together, in Britain's case as no consensus in favour of one or the other could be obtained.

There are not many types of tracked reconnaissance vehicles in service in the world today, and, of these, few are likely to survive the 1990s; as is discussed in later chapters, they tend to be more expensive, to require more maintenance and to have lower road speeds and ranges than their wheeled equivalents. Their higher noise signature, however, matters less in these days of thermal detection than was formerly the case. Because they are cheaper to acquire and to run than main battle tanks, tracked reconnaissance vehicles tend, in times of peace, to be used in training instead of MBTs, and this tendency can carry over into the early days of war, when equipment generally is in short supply, with disastrous results; they are inadequately armed and armoured for use on the modern battlefield, and one cannot help but wonder if there is a place for them in these days of helicopters and drones equipped with thermal imaging and other reconnaissance devices.

Reconnaissance Vehicle: UK
CVR(T) – Scorpion

Weight in action	8 tonnes
Crew	3
Overall length (gun front)	4.8m
Overall width	2.2m
Overall height	2.1m
Ground clearance	0.36m
Track width	0.43m
Main armament:	
calibre	76mm
stabilized (traverse/elevation)	no, manual
number of rounds carried	40
Auxiliary armament	7.62mm coaxial MG
Power plant	Jaguar 6-cyl petrol
Max. output	190bhp
Power/weight ratio	24bhp/tonne
Suspension	transverse torsion bar
Nominal ground pressure	5psi (0.36kg/cm^2)
Performance:	
max. speed (roads)	80km/hr
range (roads)	644km
fording depth	amphibious (with preparation)

Reconnaissance Vehicle: UK **Scimitar**		Main armament:		Performance:	
Weight in action	7.8 tonnes	calibre	30mm Rarden	max. speed (roads)	80km/hr
Crew	3	stabilized (traverse/elevation)	no, manual	range (roads)	644km
Overall length (gun front)	4.98m	number of rounds carried	165	fording depth	amphibious
Overall width	2.24m	Auxiliary armament	7.62mm coaxial MG		(with preparation)
Overall height	2.1m	Power plant	Jaguar 6-cyl petrol		
Ground clearance	0.36m	Power/weight ratio	25bhp/tonne		
Track width	0.43m	Suspension	transverse torsion bar		
		Nominal ground pressure	4.8psi (0.34kg/cm^2)		

Reconnaissance Vehicle: USA
CFV M-3 Bradley

Weight in action	22.7 tonnes	Track width	0.53m	Power/weight ratio	22bhp/tonne
Crew	3 plus 2	Main armament:		Suspension	transverse torsion bar
Overall length (gun front)	6.2m	calibre	25mm chain gun	Nominal ground pressure	7.4psi (0.52kg/cm^2)
Overall width	3.2m	stabilized (traverse/elevation)	yes		
Overall height	2.95m	number of rounds carried	1,500	Performance:	
Ground clearance	0.46m	Auxiliary armament	TOW missile-launcher	max. speed (roads)	66km/hr
Length of track on ground	3.9m		(twin) 7.62mm coaxial MG	range (roads)	483km
		Power plant	Cummins V-8 diesel	fording depth	amphibious
		Max. output	500bhp		

Reconnaissance Vehicle: USSR
BRM

No reproducible picture available. This vehicle appears to be based on the hull and running gear of the BMP-2 IFV, but with a larger, 2-man turret mounting a 73mm gun.

Weight in action	14.5 tonnes	Overall width	2.94m	Power plant	6-cyl in-line diesel
Crew	6	Overall height	2.1m	Max. output	300bhp
Overall length	6.75m	Ground clearance	0.39m	Power/weight ratio	20bhp/tonne
		Length of track on ground	3.5m	Suspension	torsion bar
		Track width	0.3m	Nominal ground pressure	8.4psi (0.59kg/cm^2)
		Main armament:			
		calibre	73mm	Performance:	
		stabilized (traverse/elevation)	no	max. speed (roads)	80km/hr
		number of rounds carried	39	range (roads)	500km
		Auxiliary armament	7.62mm coaxial MG	fording depth	amphibious

Specialist vehicles Special-purpose vehicles on tank chassis first made their appearance in the shape of salvage tanks, fitted with a crane for the lifting of heavy components, during the First World War. Two were completed by the British and put into service in France, where they were used in the recovery and repair of fighting tanks.

During the Second World War they proliferated, particularly in Major-General Sir Percy Hobart's 79th Armoured Division and its successor, the Specialized Armour Development Establishment (SADE), whose products were known as 'Funnies'. Developed primarily for the invasion of north-west Europe, they included demolition vehicles, gap-crossing equipment, mine-clearing vehicles, beach ARVs, soft ground crossing aids, dozer tanks, flame-throwing tanks and ARVs of all types. Specialist AA tanks and self-propelled field, medium and anti-tank artillery were also much used,

as indeed they still are, but these are covered in a companion volume in this series rather than here.

Today and for the forseeable future, the main specialist vehicles are armoured recovery vehicles (ARVs), armoured bridge-layers (AVLBs) and specialized Engineer/Pioneer vehicles such as the British Armoured Vehicle Royal Engineers (AVRE).

Recovery vehicles are generally provided with a built-in winch in place of the tank turret, an hydraulically-operated crane capable of lifting the heaviest assembly of the vehicles likely to be recovered (usually the power pack), an hydraulically-operated spade/dozer blade and space for replacement assemblies and the recovery crew. Most modern ARVs are descended in principle from the German wartime recovery vehicle based upon the Panther tank, the Pz Berge Wg Panther. ARVs tend to be on the chassis of the heaviest tracked vehicle in the unit which they are serving; this is partly

for logistic reasons of commonality of parts, and mainly because they need the same mobility and level of protection as the vehicle for whose recovery and repair they are responsible.

Bridge-laying tanks generally fall into one of three types; the first folds its bridge in scissors form for travelling, unfolding it to lay it across the obstacle; the second folds and lays its bridge telescopically, and the third carries a rigid bridge and lays it in one piece. The British, French and US favour the first and the West Germans the second type; the Soviet Army used the third type, mechanically launched by chain drive rather than hydraulically, until the 1970s, when they introduced a modern scissors bridge based on the T-55 chassis. Bridge-layers do not need, as does the ARV, to keep up with the MBTs in an advance, and they can therefore be, and usually are, mounted on obsolescent rather than the latest tank chassis.

Engineer vehicles are generally based on the hull and chassis of current tanks, although sometimes, as in the case of the British Combat Engineer Tractor (CET), they are purpose-designed *ab initio*. Often similar to the ARV, they tend additionally to carry an earth auger and scarifying dozer blades. The British AVRE and CET are different from the continental concept of an engineer vehicle, however; the former carries a 165mm calibre demolition gun, firing HESH ammunition, in the turret of a Centurion tank Mark 5 in place of the normal armament, a fascine for crossing deep ditches or wadis and an hydraulically-operated dozer blade, while the latter, which has largely superseded the AVRE in the British Army, is a light armoured amphibious tractor equipped with a rocket-propelled earth anchor and a winch, for exiting from rivers, as well as an hydraulically-operated scarifying dozer/bucket blade.

Specialist Vehicle: Federal Germany
Bergepanzer 2 (ARV)

Weight in action	39.8 tonnes
Crew	4
Overall length	7.45m
Overall width	3.25m
Overall height	2.7m
Ground clearance	0.44m
Length of track on ground	4.24m
Track width	0.55m
Load capacity	0.6 tonnes
Armament	2×7.62mm MG
Power plant	MTU V-10 diesel Type MB 838
Max. output	830bhp
Power/weight ratio	21bhp/tonne
Suspension	torsion bar
Nominal ground pressure	12psi (0.85kg/cm^2)
Performance:	
max. speed (roads)	62km/hr
max. speed (reverse)	24km/hr
range (roads)	500km
fording depth	4m (with preparation)
Recovery equipment includes:	
winch	
crane	hydraulic operation
dozer blade/spade	

Specialist Vehicle: Federal Germany
Pionierpanzer 'Standard' (Engineer Vehicle)

Weight in action	40.8 tonnes
Crew	4
Overall length	7.88m
Overall width	3.25m
Overall height	2.7m
Ground clearance	0.44m
Length of track on ground	4.24m
Track width	0.55m
Load capacity	0.6 tonne
Armament	2×7.62mm MG
Power plant	MTU V-10 diesel Type MB 838
Max. output	830bhp
Power/weight ratio	20bhp/tonne
Suspension	torsion bar
Nominal ground pressure	12.4psi (0.87kg/cm^2)
Performance:	
max. speed (roads)	62km/hr
range (roads)	800km
fording depth	4m (with preparation)
Engineer equipment includes:	
winch	
crane	hydraulically operated
auger	
dozer blade	

Specialist Vehicle: Federal Germany

Biber AVLB

Weight in action (incl. bridge)	45 tonnes
(excl. bridge)	35 tonnes
Crew	2
Gap spanned	20m
Military load capacity of bridge	50 tonnes
Overall length (incl. bridge)	11.4m
(excl. bridge)	10.2m
Overall width (incl. bridge)	4m
(excl. bridge)	3.25m
Overall height (incl. bridge)	3.5m
(excl. bridge)	2.56m
Ground clearance	0.44m
Length of track on ground	4.24m
Track width	0.55m
Power plant	MTU MB838 V-10 diesel
Max. output	830bhp
Power/weight ratio	19.7bhp/tonne
Suspension	torsion bar
Nominal ground pressure	13.7psi (0.96kg/cm^2)
Performance:	
max. speed (roads)	62km/hr
range (roads)	800km
fording depth	1.7m (with preparation)

Specialist Vehicle: UK

Chieftain Mk 6 AVLB

Weight in action	53.3 tonnes
Crew	3
Gap spanned	22m
Military load capacity of bridge	70 tonnes
Overall length (incl. bridge)	13.74m
(excl. bridge)	7.52m
Overall width (incl. bridge)	4.17m
(excl. bridge)	3.5m
Overall height (incl. bridge)	3.92m
Ground clearance	0.5m
Length of track on ground	4.8m
Track width	0.61m
Armament	2×7.62mm MG
Power plant	Leyland 6-cyl opposed piston L-60 2-stroke
Max. output	750bhp
Power/weight ratio	13.6bhp/tonne
Suspension	Horstmann coil spring bogie
Nominal ground pressure	11.9psi (0.84kg/cm^2)
Performance:	
max. speed (roads)	43km/hr
range (roads)	400km
fording depth	1.07m

Note: These figures relate to the Chieftain AVLB equipped with the No. 8 Tank Bridge. The No. 9 Tank Bridge, with which it can also be equipped, spans a gap of up to 12.2m, with firm banks.

Specialist Vehicle: UK
Challenger ARRV

Weight in action	62 tonnes
Weight in action (with spare power pack)	67.5 tonnes
Crew	5 (plus 2)
Overall length	9.64m
Overall width	3.55m
Overall height	2.96m
Overall height (incl. spare power pack)	3.91m
Ground clearance	0.5m
Track width	0.65m
Load capacity'	6 tonnes
Armament	7.62mm MG
Power plant	Rolls-Royce CV12 12-cyl diesel
Max. output	1,200bhp
Power/weight ratio	20bhp/tonne
Suspension	hydro-gas
Nominal ground pressure (less spare power pack)	13.6psi (0.96kg/cm^2)

Performance:
max. speed (roads)	59km/hr
range (roads)	500km
fording depth	1.07m

Recovery equipment includes: crane, main winch, auxiliary winch, earth anchor/dozer/stabilizer blade, welding and air tools

Specialist Vehicle: UK
Warrior WCRV (Repair & Recovery Vehicle)

Weight in action	28.5 tonnes
Crew	5
Overall length	6.68m
Overall width	3.13m
Overall height	2.8m
Ground clearance	0.49m
Length of track on ground	3.82m
Track width	0.46m
Armament	7.62mm chain gun
Power plant	Perkins Rolls-Royce V-8 diesel
Max. output	550bhp
Power/weight ratio	19.3bhp/tonne
Suspension	transverse torsion bar w/rotary dampers
Nominal ground pressure	12.1psi (0.85kg/cm^2)

Performance:
max. speed (roads)	70km/hr
range (roads)	500km
fording depth	1.3m

Recovery and repair equipment includes: hydraulic crane, winch, earth anchor and suspension lock-out

Specialist Vehicle: UK
Combat Engineer Tractor (CET)

Weight in action	17.8 tonnes	Track width	0.5m	max speed (water)	5knots
Crew	2	Armament	7.62mm MG	range (roads)	480km
Overall length	7.54m	Power plant	Rolls-Royce C6 6-cyl	fording depth	amphibious
Overall width (over bucket)	2.9m	Max. output	320bhp	Additional features:	
Width over hull	2.79m	Power/weight ratio	18bhp/tonne	2 steerable water jets for propulsion in	
Overall height	2.67m	Suspension	torsion bar	water,	
Ground clearance	0.46m	Nominal ground pressure	6.6psi (0.46kg/ cm^2)	rocket-propelled earth anchor,	
Length of track on ground	3.6m	Performance:		digging/dozing bucket,	
		max. speed (roads)	56km/hr	winch,	
				4 forward and 4 reverse speeds	

Wheeled vehicles

Armoured personnel carriers Wheeled armoured personnel carriers are possibly the least complicated and the most numerous of wheeled armoured vehicles. They are used as armoured buses for the transport of infantry and as armoured command vehicles for commanders and staff, and generally provide protection only against small arms ball and AP ammunition and HE shell fragments. They consist generally of lightly armoured box bodies, either on commercial four-wheel drive vehicle chassis or on versions specially strengthened and modified for military service. Their cross-country capacity is for the most part minimal, depend-

Armoured Personnel Carrier (Wheeled): Federal Germany Transportpanzer 1 (FUCHS)				
Weight in action	17 tonnes	Overall height	2.3m	
Crew	2	Ground clearance	0.4m	
Personnel capacity	10	Wheelbase	1.75mm + 2.05m	
Configuration	6×6	Track:		
Overall length	6.76m	front	2.54m	
Overall width	2.98m	rear	2.56m	

Overall height	2.3m	
Ground clearance	0.4m	
Wheelbase	1.75mm + 2.05m	
Track:		
front	2.54m	
rear	2.56m	
Armament	7.62mm MG or 20mm cannon	
Power plant	Mercedes Benz V-8 OM 402A 8-cyl diesel	
Max. output	320bhp	
Power/weight ratio	18.8bhp/tonne	
Suspension	coil spring and fluid damper	
Performance:		
max. speed (roads)	105km/hr	
max. speed (water)	10.5km/hr	
range (roads)	800km	
fording depth	amphibious	
Water propulsion	twin screw	

ing greatly upon the number of driven wheels and the vertical movement their springing system allows them. Their advantage lies in their ability rapidly and cheaply to move large numbers of infantry over fairly large distances in reasonable comfort with some protection.

Few, if any, of the vehicles currently in service with the armies of the major powers are likely to survive into the 21st century, but those of West Germany, the UK and the USSR, among the more recent introductions, are included here as examples. Vehicles entering service after the year 2000 are likely to continue to be based on the then current range of commercial multi-wheeled drive vehicles, using as many of their components as possible.

Armoured Personnel Carrier (Wheeled):		Overall width	2.5m	Power plant	GM Bedford 6-cyl diesel
UK		Overall height	2.65m	Max. output	167bhp
Saxon (AT105)		Ground clearance	0.33m (to axle)	Power/weight ratio	14.3bhp/tonne
Weight in action	11.66 tonnes	Wheelbase	3.12m	Suspension	leaf springs
Crew	2	Track:		Performance:	
Personnel capacity	8–10	front	2.06m	max. speed (roads)	87km/hr
Configuration	4×4	rear	2.12m	range (roads)	434km
Overall length	5.34m	Armament	7.62mm MG	fording depth	0.75m

Armoured Personnel Carrier (Wheeled):		Ground clearance	0.4m	fording depth	amphibious (hydro-jet
USSR		Wheelbase	1.4m + 1.8m + 1.4m		propulsion)
BTR-70		Armament	14.5mm heavy MG & 7.62mm	*Note*: A later version, the BTR-80, entered	
Weight in action	11.5 tonnes		coaxial	production in the early 1980s. Externally	
Crew	3	Power plant	twin petrol engines	little different from the BTR-70, the main	
Personnel capacity	8	Max. output	2×115bhp	improvement is the substitution of a single	
Configuration	8×8	Power/weight ratio	20bhp/tonne	260bhp diesel engine in place of the twin	
Overall length	7.54m	Performance:		petrol engines of the BTR-70.	
Overall width	2.8m	max. speed (roads)	80km/hr		
Overall height	2.23m	range (roads)	400km		

Reconnaissance vehicles It is in the field of reconnaissance, particularly deep reconnaissance, that the wheeled AFV comes into its own. The equivalent of the earlier horsed cavalry, it is used in much the same way, by reconnaissance units often formed from cavalry regiments. Lightly armoured, the wheeled reconnaissance vehicle depends for its security on its speed, low silhouette, small outline and its relative silence as compared to tracked vehicles. It is capable of high road speeds and has a long range, due to its greater fuel economy; it is generally armed, but its armament is not heavy enough to enable it to fight for information. It is favoured over the tracked vehicle in the internal security role because of its lower profile and less aggressive appearance. Its cross-country capacity is directly related to the number of driven wheels and the vertical wheel movement permitted by its suspension.

There has been a prejudice against wheeled reconnaissance in the US Army since the Second World War and none is at present in its vehicle inventory. In the FRG, on the other hand, armoured reconnaissance vehicles have been exclusively wheeled since the formation of the Bundeswehr in the 1950s. In Britain, France and the USSR, both wheeled and tracked armoured reconnaissance vehicles have been, and continue to be, employed alongside one another. Much of the reconnaissance formerly carried out by armoured reconnaissance vehicles is now performed by reconnaissance drones, aircraft (both fixed and rotary wing) and even satellites. Modern surveillance aids such as battlefield surveillance radar, thermal imaging and other devices have further reduced the scope for the employment of this formerly essential vehicle, at least in north-west Europe. Of the very many varieties of this most universal vehicle currently in service throughout the world, few will survive into the 21st century in front-line armies. The three most interesting and with most potential for development have been selected for inclusion here; these are the French AMX-10 6-wheeled skid steer vehicle, the British Fox and the Soviet BRDM-2.

Reconnaissance Vehicle (Wheeled): France **AMX-10RC**		Wheelbase	1.55m + 1.55m	Power/weight ratio	16.5bhp/tonne
		Track	2.43m	Suspension	hydro-gas
Weight in action	15.8 tonnes	Main armament:		Performance:	
Crew	4	calibre	105mm	max. speed (roads)	85km/hr
Configuration	6×6, skid steer	length in calibres	48	max. speed (water)	7km/hr
Overall length (gun front)	9.2m	number of rounds carried	38	range (roads)	800km
Overall width	2.95m	Auxiliary armament	7.62mm MG coaxial	fording depth	amphibious (twin water
Overall height	2.68m	Power plant	Hispano HS115 8-cyl diesel		jets)
Ground clearance	0.2–0.6m adjustable	Max. output	260bhp		

Reconnaissance Vehicle (Wheeled):	Ground clearance	0.4m	
Federal Germany	Wheelbase	1.4m + 2.4m + 1.4m	
Spähpanzer 'Luchs'	Track	2.54m	
Weight in action	19.5 tonnes	Main armament:	
Crew	4	calibre	20mm
Configuration	8×8	number of rounds carried	375
Overall length	7.74m	Auxiliary armament	7.62mm MG
Overall width	2.98m	Power plant	Daimler Benz V-10 diesel
Overall height	2.9m	Max. output	390bhp

Power/weight ratio	20bhp/tonne		
Suspension	coil spring/w/fluid damper		
Performance:			
max. speed (roads)	90km/hr, forward & reverse		
max. speed (water)	9km/hr, twin propeller drive		
range (roads)	800km		
fording depth	amphibious		

Reconnaissance Vehicle (Wheeled): UK
CVR(W) – Fox

Weight in action	6.4 tonnes	Ground clearance	0.3m	Power/weight ratio	29.8bhp/tonne
Crew	3	Wheelbase	2.46m	Suspension	coil spring fluid damper
Configuration	4×4	Track	1.75m	Performance:	
Overall length (gun front)	5.36m	Main armament:		max. speed (roads)	104km/hr
Overall width	2.13m	calibre	30mm, Rarden	max. speed (water)	5.3km/hr
Overall height	2.2m	number of rounds carried	99	range (roads)	430km
		Auxiliary armament	7.62mm coaxial MG	fording depth	amphibious (with
		Power plant	Jaguar XK 6-cyl petrol		preparation)

Reconnaissance Vehicle: USSR						
BRDM-2		Ground clearance	0.35m	Suspension	leaf spring/fluid damper	
Weight in action	7 tonnes	Wheelbase	3.1m	Performance:		
Crew	4	Main armament:		max. speed (roads)	95km/hr	
Configuration	4×4	calibre	14.5mm MG	max. speed (water)	5km/hr	
Overall length	5.75m	number of rounds carried	500	range (roads)	750km	
Overall width	2.35m	Auxiliary armament	7.62mm coaxial MG	fording depth	amphibious (single water	
Overall height	2.31m	Power plant	GAZ-41 V-8 petrol		jet)	
		Power/weight ratio	20bhp/tonne			

FIREPOWER

It must never be forgotten that firepower is the only reason for the tank's existence; it is around its firepower that the rest of the tank is designed, with the sole aim of enabling fire to be brought to bear on the enemy wherever and whenever it is required. To enable this to be done, the tank's armament is mounted on a vehicle with maximum mobility, and its crew is given sufficient protection against enemy weapons to enable it to continue to bring its armament to bear effectively upon the enemy at all times, even when under enemy fire.

Tank armament has changed as the tank's role has changed, over the 70 years since its first action at Flers-Courcelette in September 1916; this was only to be expected, since the intended role of an AFV dictates its design characteristics and its specification. Originally designed to counter the stagnation of trench warfare, the tank was armed with direct fire weapons for killing personnel and demolishing strongpoints while crossing the enemy trenches; the 'male' heavy tanks mounted two naval 6-pounder guns of 57mm calibre in sponsons projecting some three feet from the side of the tank, one on each side. These guns fired high-explosive (HE) shells, armour-piercing solid shot and case shot for short-range anti-personnel purposes. The highly effective case-shot projectile was filled with steel balls and had a small bursting charge fuzed to explode on impact; it was preferred to HE for the engagement of troops in the open, since engagements were at very short range. The 6-pounders had a limited traverse arc, controlled by a handwheel operated by the gunner, and were controlled in elevation by the gunner's shoulder. In addition to the 6-pounders, the male tanks carried a number of machine guns, mounted in the front, rear and on both sides; the 'female' version carried two Vickers water-cooled machine-guns in each sponson in place of the 6-pounders, as well as the Hotchkiss or Lewis guns carried by the male. In the design of the tank and its armament, therefore, the emphasis was on the killing of men and the reduction of their fortifications and emplacements, rather than on the attack of enemy tanks.

The Germans too, in their A7V tank, selected a calibre of 57mm for the main gun, but the French mounted the famous 75mm 'soixante-quinze' field gun, first introduced into service in 1897, in their Saint Chamond heavy tank. The French choice of calibre was much more suitable for a weapon intended to fire HE shells in the anti-personnel role; below this calibre, a high-explosive shell is too small to be able to contain sufficient explosive to have much effect at the target. For the tank versus tank actions later in the war, however, the 6-pounder firing solid shot was more effective than the 75mm.

It is unfortunate that the memories of these more recent actions obscured the original real aim and purpose of the tank in military thinking, both in Britain and in France, between the wars and well into the Second World War; the result was that the tank v. tank role began to assume undue importance, and the main armament of infantry (assault), medium, cruiser and even light tanks became an anti-tank weapon firing high-velocity armour-piercing shot. Unfortunately, until quite late in the Second World War all anti-tank weapons were of a calibre less than 3 inches (76.2mm), and it was therefore necessary to provide alternative weapons for the firing of HE shell. In the British Army, this at first took the form of a 3-inch howitzer, interchangeable in the tank with the anti-tank weapon, or mounted in the hull, with limited traverse, in addition to it. In US tanks, a 75mm gun was hull-mounted for the same reason, while the Germans mounted a 75mm gun in their Pz Kpfw IV from its introduction in the late 1930s for the HE-firing anti-personnel role.

With the inevitable increases in anti-tank gun calibre, size and weight resulting from the up-armouring of tanks during the war, the field anti-tank gun on a wheeled carriage became too unwieldy and conspicuous and the tank, with its tracked carriage, became the obvious alternative mounting. Thus the tank's tank v. tank role was perpetuated because the tank, or its tracked chassis, was the only carrier able to provide the necessary mobility for the large guns required to penetrate the armour of the opposing side's tanks. Such guns had calibres in excess of 3 inches, and were thus capable of firing a very effective weight of HE shell as well as various types of anti-armour projectile.

The gun is a very effective weapon with many advantages, but the compromises in design of gun, mounting and recoil gear needed to enable it to combine the two functions of tank- and man-killing reduce its effectiveness in both roles. To make the killing of other tanks the primary role of the tank is wasteful, and implies that, were the enemy not to possess tanks, we should have no need of them ourselves; this is obvious nonsense, and the tank's

◄ A good example of a self-propelled anti-tank gun, in this case the German Jagdpanther (Panther tank-hunter) of the Second World War. By removing the Panther tank turret and limiting gun traverse, it was possible to mount a gun of larger calibre and higher performance while at the same time lowering the vehicle height. (Author's collection)

► This photograph of a Challenger MBT clearly shows the housing for the muzzle reflector sight (MRS), the thermal sleeve and the fume extractor on the gun barrel. (RAC Centre)

main role of killing personnel should never be forgotten. Tanks cannot hold ground; only infantry can do so, suitably supported by other arms, and it is the ground-holding infantry who will be the main obstacle to the advance of opposing forces, and who should be the main target for tanks. There is an undoubted role for tracked self-propelled anti-tank weapons in the army inventory, but these are not tanks and are less expensive than tanks, although they would work closely with them.

By the end of the Second World War, the primarily anti-tank role for tanks had become accepted doctrine by all the combatant countries, and the tank guns for fulfilling this role became ever larger in calibre and longer in barrel length; having started the war with anti-tank calibres of 37mm to 40mm, they ended it with calibres ranging from 75mm up to 128mm, and barrel lengths had increased proportionately. These large increases were due to the means by which the anti-tank projectile punched holes in tank armour, employing the kinetic energy (KE) stored in the projectile due to its weight (mass) and the velocity which it has attained at the time it strikes the armour. In fact, the kinetic energy is proportional to the velocity squared, multiplied by the mass (weight), so that a small increase in striking velocity will give a greater increase in KE than an increase in weight. The longer

the gun barrel from which a projectile is fired, the greater will be the velocity with which it leaves the gun muzzle (muzzle velocity, or MV) for a given weight of projectile and propellant charge, so that the reason for the increase in barrel length can readily be understood. The diagram shows how muzzle velocity increases with barrel length, here expressed in 'calibres'; it can be seen that, even with a barrel length of 100 calibres, the MV is still increasing. At this sort of length, however, the barrel becomes too flexible to be accurate, and other means of attaining high and very high projectile velocity have to be employed.

At the high velocities required by anti-tank KE projectiles, the time of flight from the shot leaving the gun muzzle to its striking the target is very short, from 1 to 4 seconds depending on range, and gives the target little time to take evasive action, even if it has seen the gun flash; this is one of the advantages of the gun as an anti-tank weapon. The energy transmitted to the gun on firing is, however, very large, and the recoil gear to absorb this energy is heavy, large and complicated; recoil length must be so adjusted that the breech of the recoiling gun will not hit turret roof or other items, but must be great enough to activate the semi-automatic gear for opening the gun breech and ejecting the empty cartridge case (if any). The ejected case sucks noxious fumes back into the turret as it leaves the breech unless measures are taken to prevent this; a simple device, invented and first used by the British but now used world-wide, is the fume extractor, consisting of a concentric cylinder mounted about halfway along the gun barrel covering a series of radial drillings in the barrel. This cylinder acts as a chamber for holding the propellant gases while the empty case is ejected, allowing them to follow the projectile out of the muzzle when this has happened.

Unlike the anti-tank KE projectile, high-explosive shell of all kinds require a lower firing and striking velocity; this is partly because the shell is thin-walled, partly because the shell needs a fuze to detonate it,

which must function in the very short time between the shell striking the target and it being broken up on impact, and partly because the effect of the shell at the target is independent of velocity. HE shell and other chemical energy projectiles, therefore, need less propellant than KE projectiles and could make do with a smaller cartridge case and gun chamber than is required by high-velocity KE ammunition; for the sake of standardization, however, cartridge cases for both natures must be the same size. The lower muzzle velocity of the HE and other chemical energy projectiles aggravates the problem of operating the semi-automatic breech opening gear, as the recoil of the gun

◄ Typical rounds of fixed ammunition in which the projectile is fixed in the cartridge case, thus enabling both to be stowed and loaded into the gun as one item. (MoD)

► Separate ammunition, for the 120mm guns of Chieftain and Challenger, in which the projectile is loaded into the gun separately from, and before, the bagged propellant charge, two types of which are shown on the left. (MoD)

is so much less than with KE ammunition, and this is another problem resulting from the design compromises necessary with modern tank guns.

The whole history of tank gun development has thus been influenced by the conflicting requirements for firing anti-tank and anti-personnel ammunition. The anti-personnel requirement is the more important, but the anti-tank is the more exacting. A high-explosive shell may produce some effect even if it is not a direct hit; even the smallest HE shell will do some damage to personnel. On the other hand, an armour-piercing projectile is only effective if it is a direct hit, and even then its remaining energy may be insufficient to do serious damage. Anti-tank weapons firing KE projectiles are heavier, longer and shorter-lived than comparable anti-personnel weapons.

If a projectile could be devised that was equally effective against both armour and personnel, the gun could be designed around it and the need for compromise in designing a dual-purpose weapon would disappear. The mention of other chemical energy projectiles brings us to alternative methods of defeating armour, which can be employed with guns as well as with relatively low-velocity weapons such as infantry anti-tank projectors and anti-tank guided missiles, and which have a limited anti-personnel effect as well.

The first of these in chronological order is the hollow-charge or High-Explosive Anti-Tank (HEAT) shell, first employed, both in guns, recoilless guns and infantry anti-tank projectors, by both sides during the Second World War. This incorporates, within the shell casing, a soft metal cone with its base towards the nose of the shell around which is moulded the high-explosive charge, and, projecting from the shell nose, a delicate fuze arranged to detonate the charge at a set distance (the stand-off distance) from the armour plate target. When the fuze initiates the HE charge, the cone shape forms the detonation into a plasma jet which literally melts its way through a thickness of armour some three to six times the calibre of the shell. It is so effective against conventional steel armour materials that no tank could carry sufficient steel armour to defeat the modern HEAT projectile and remain mobile; hence the development of modern composite armour materials such as 'Chobham' armour, mentioned in a later Chapter. Despite its HE content, however, the HEAT projectile is not very effective in the anti-personnel role, if only because of its highly directional effect and its less frangible, more ductile casing which does not lend itself to fragmentation. Being dependent for its effect at the target on chemical rather than kinetic energy, its armour penetration is independent of its velocity; provided the target is hit, it will be penetrated. In addition, the sensitive fuzing requires that its striking velocity be low, which means that its muzzle velocity must also be low, leading to the same problems in a gun designed to fire high-velocity KE ammunition as are posed by HE shell. The biggest disadvantage to firing HEAT projectiles from a rifled gun, however, is the degradation of penetration performance resulting from spinning the projectile; this is so marked that much design effort and ingenuity has been devoted around the world, without great success, to developing methods of nullifying the spin imparted by the rifling. HEAT and hyper-velocity KE projectiles are the two standard methods of defeating armour from tank guns throughout the world today.

The second type of chemical energy anti-armour projectile is peculiar to the British and is known as High-Explosive Squash Head (HESH). In this projectile, the high-explosive charge is contained in a thin-walled, highly ductile casing; on striking the target, the casing and explosive charge squash and spread over its surface, when the charge is detonated. On detonation the explosive, which is in contact with the armour, sends shock waves through it and detaches a 'scab' of armour from the rear face; this careers at high velocity round the inside of the target vehicle, in theory doing as much damage as penetration by a KE projectile. As with the HEAT, the HESH projectile is fired at a relatively low velocity, in order that striking velocity is low enough for the fuze to function correctly. Again, effect at the target is independent of striking velocity; if the projectile hits the target, damage will be done. Unfortunately, however, any air gap between the detonating shell and the target armour plate will nullify the effect of HESH; also, because of the ductility of its shell casing, it is not a very effective anti-personnel weapon, giving plenty of blast but not much in the way of fragmentation. In addition, should it hit soft ground

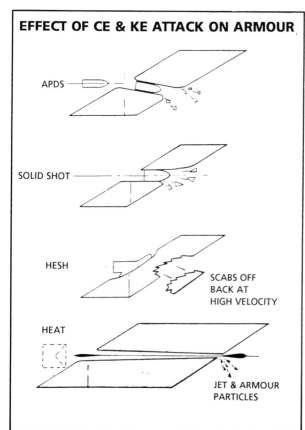

EFFECT OF CE & KE ATTACK ON ARMOUR

APDS

SOLID SHOT

HESH — SCABS OFF BACK AT HIGH VELOCITY

HEAT — JET & ARMOUR PARTICLES

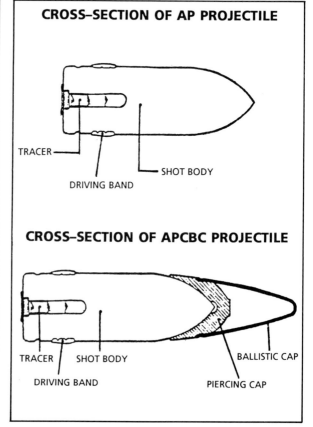

CROSS–SECTION OF AP PROJECTILE

TRACER
DRIVING BAND
SHOT BODY

CROSS–SECTION OF APCBC PROJECTILE

TRACER
DRIVING BAND
SHOT BODY
BALLISTIC CAP
PIERCING CAP

it will often fail to detonate, or will detonate so deep in the ground that the blast is directed harmlessly upwards. It is, however, most effective against concrete fortifications, the task for which it was first developed.

The other type of chemical energy projectile is the smoke projectile, used for masking off enemy positions to enable one's own troops to move undetected. As with the other three types already described, the muzzle and striking velocities with this type of ammunition are low, in order both that the fuze will function correctly and that the shell will not bury itself so deeply in the ground that the smoke being ejected from its base will rise straight up in the air rather than spreading in a satisfactory screen. With all chemical energy ammunition, the relatively low muzzle velocity results in the shell having a high, somewhat parabolic trajectory; this means that, for accurate fire, accurate range estimation is essential. With the flat trajectory and short time of flight of the high-velocity KE projectile, however,

accurate range estimation, particularly at ranges out to 2,000 metres, is less important than other sources of error; these will be discussed in more detail later in this chapter.

The earliest kinetic energy anti-armour projectiles were full-calibre solid shot, with an ogival nose to reduce air resistance, the only pyrotechnic content of which was the tracer contained in a drilling in the base. This type of projectile was known as AP (armour-piercing) and it was fired at moderate MVs in the range 2,000–2,700 feet per second; it worked reasonably well until it came up against sloped armour, off which it tended to richochet after making a mere scoop in the armour. With the increasing use of thicker, sloped armour as the Second World War progressed, a softer metal cap was placed over the nose of the shot; on striking the target, this cap deformed and acted to straighten the shot so that it struck the armour at approximately 90°, thus giving it a greater chance to

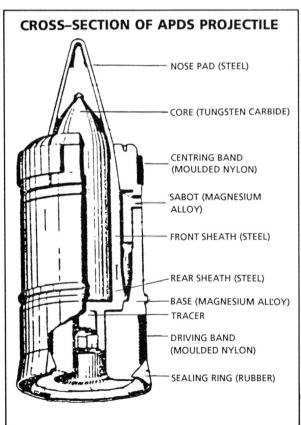

CROSS–SECTION OF APDS PROJECTILE

NOSE PAD (STEEL)

CORE (TUNGSTEN CARBIDE)

CENTRING BAND (MOULDED NYLON)

SABOT (MAGNESIUM ALLOY)

FRONT SHEATH (STEEL)

REAR SHEATH (STEEL)

BASE (MAGNESIUM ALLOY)

TRACER

DRIVING BAND (MOULDED NYLON)

SEALING RING (RUBBER)

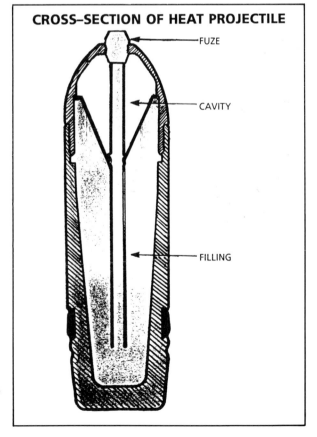

CROSS–SECTION OF HEAT PROJECTILE

FUZE

CAVITY

FILLING

penetrate the plate. The cap also helped to reduce the shattering of AP shot when striking face-hardened armour. This type of shot was known as 'armour-piercing capped' (APC) and was fired at MVs similar to those of straight AP; the cap added considerably to the air resistance met by the APC shot in flight, so that another, ballistic light metal cap was added over the nose to streamline the shot. This type of shot was known as 'armour-piercing capped, ballistic cap' or, much better, as APCBC for short.

As armour thicknesses and angles of slope further increased during the Second World War, ways of increasing the muzzle velocity and the density of shot were investigated by both sides in order to increase armour penetration without having to re-gun their tank fleets. Both Germans and British opted for composite-rigid designs, in which a sub-calibre penetrator of dense material such as tungsten carbide was contained in a full calibre jacket carrying the driving bands; in the British design, the jacket or 'sabot' disintegrated on leaving the gun muzzle, having imparted its high MV to the dense tungsten carbide core which carried on alone to strike the target. This type of projectile is known as 'armour-piercing discarding sabot (APDS), and was, until recently, the standard armour-piercing ammunition of British MBTs. The German solution involved a full-calibre mild steel projectile body, in skeleton form and with a ballistic cap; this body carried the driving bands and contained a tungsten carbide core, both body and core carrying on to the target together. This type of projectile was known as 'armour-piercing, composite rigid' or AP/CR, but did not achieve the high velocities of APDS, and velocity tended to drop off at the longer ranges due to its poor ballistic shape. Development was, in any case, hindered by the wartime shortage of tungsten in Germany.

In recent years, kinetic energy APDS projectiles have tended towards fin instead of spin stabilization, with long rod penetrators of tungsten alloy or depleted uranium, fitted with light alloy fins and ballistic cap, carried in a light alloy discarding sabot with plastic driving band (for rifled guns) or obturator (for smooth-bore guns). This family of projectiles is known by the generic title of 'armour-piercing fin-stabilized discarding sabot' (APFSDS), and they achieve muzzle velocities in the region of 5,000 feet per second (ft/sec). There is thus a tendency in both chemical energy and kinetic energy anti-tank ammunition to dispense with the

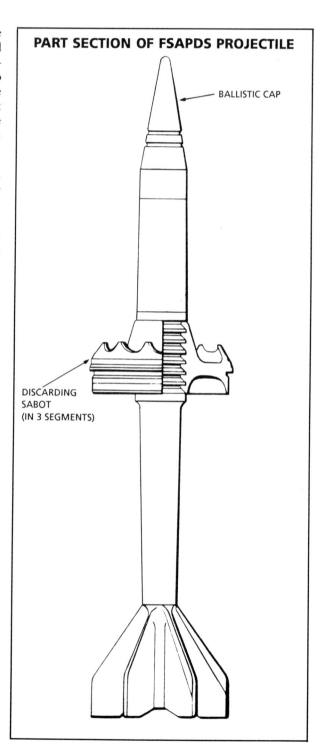

PART SECTION OF FSAPDS PROJECTILE

BALLISTIC CAP

DISCARDING SABOT (IN 3 SEGMENTS)

rifled gun barrel in order to take advantage of the improved armour penetration performance of modern fin-stabilized projectiles; it will be remembered that the armour penetration of HEAT projectiles is positively downgraded by spinning of the projectile, and its performance can only benefit from fin stabilization. In view of this, the great military powers of NATO and the Warsaw Pact, with the exception of Britain, have changed their MBT main armament from rifled to smooth-bore guns, thus reducing barrel wear and increasing barrel life as well as improving their guns' performance.

Why Britain should be the only country in step is not at all clear; the 'not invented here' (NIH) syndrome obviously plays some part, and the vested interests of the Government-owned Royal Armament Research and Development Establishment (RARDE), responsible for the design and development of all guns and ammunition in the British Army, dictate that British rather than foreign designs of weapon should be taken into British service wherever possible. The rifled gun, with its shorter life, greater wear and inaccuracy that increases with wear, is a positive disadvantage when firing HEAT or any form of spin-stabilized projectile; the special materials, heat treatment and machining processes required to produce a rifled gun with increased life add considerably and unnecessarily to the cost per barrel.

The excuse is advanced, and we have seen it repeated in the argument over whether the British Army should replace its Chieftain fleet with the US Abrams or the Challenger 2 proposed by Vickers Defence Systems, that it is uneconomic and logistically unacceptable to have two different types of MBT gun ammunition in service at the same time. This argument is, of course, nonsense; it happened when the British Army up-gunned its Centurion fleet from the 20-pounder (84mm) to the 105mm, and again when Chieftain, with its 120mm gun, was introduced alongside the Centurion. It is still happening in the US and West German Armies, where the 120mm-armed Abrams and Leopard 2 are in service with the 105mm guns of the M-60 and Leopard 1, and has happened in the Soviet Army, that most pragmatic of organizations, with the introduction of the 125mm smooth-bore gun of the T-64, T-72 and T-80 alongside both the 100mm rifled gun of the T-55 and the 115mm smooth-bore of the T-62.

Whether rifled or smooth-bore, however, the modern MBT main armament gun is a very long-barrelled weapon of large calibre, requiring rounds of ammunition that are both long and heavy. Until recently, all tank gun ammunition was 'fixed'; in other words, the projectile was crimped into the cartridge case and the complete round was stowed, and loaded into the gun breech, in one piece. The cartridge case was made out of some malleable metal such as brass, and contained the propellant charge and the primer with which the charge was initiated; when the propellant was ignited, the rapid expansion of the gases produced the kick at the rear of the projectile which propelled it up the barrel and, at the same time, expanded the cartridge case so as to seal, or obturate, the breech to prevent any propellant gas escaping rearwards. The fixed round has served its purpose very well, enabling rapid rates of fire to be obtained; the Centurion frequently demonstrated its ability to engage and hit twelve different targets at different ranges in the space of one minute. As calibres increased, however, the weight and loading length of the round increased also, to the point where the standard NATO (based upon the British) 105mm tank gun round was about as much as one man could handle, and was about as long as could be conveniently accommodated within the turret behind the gun breech when being loaded.

As the 100mm–105mm gun MBTs have been replaced by their successors mounting guns of 115mm, 120mm and 125mm calibre, the extra length and weight of the ammunition has dictated that projectile and propellant should be separated, necessitating the separate loading of the two items. While this increases loading time and marginally reduces rate of fire, it produces benefits in ease of stowage, less fatigue for the loader, and reduction of fire risk. In the British 120mm Chieftain and Challenger, the propellant is contained in a bag, which is consumed with the propellant when the gun is fired; this type of ammunition is known as 'separate' to distinguish it from fixed ammunition. As the charge bag is consumable, there are no empty cartridge cases to be disposed of after firing and no fumes sucked back into the fighting compartment by the ejected case, as occurs with fixed ammunition.

To enable it to fire separate ammunition, particularly where the charge container is consumed with the charge, the gun breech needs to be redesigned so that obturation is obtained by means other than the cartridge case; it can also be simplified in another respect as there is no case to be ejected automatically after

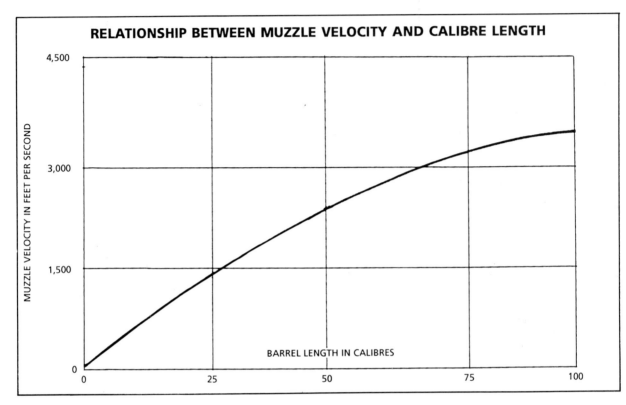

RELATIONSHIP BETWEEN MUZZLE VELOCITY AND CALIBRE LENGTH

MUZZLE VELOCITY IN FEET PER SECOND

BARREL LENGTH IN CALIBRES

firing. Tank guns firing fixed ammunition have all had breeches with vertical or sideways sliding wedge breech-blocks; these closed automatically as the round was loaded, and opened automatically as the gun recoiled, automatically ejecting the empty cartridge case in doing so. The breech of the Chieftain/Challenger gun is opened semi-automatically, and incorporates a novel method of obturation within the vertically sliding breech-block. Other countries employing guns of around this calibre have also changed from fixed to separate ammunition, with semi-combustible cases in the 120mm smooth-bore Rheinmetall gun in the Leopard 2 and Abrams M1A1, with cased charges in the Soviet 115mm smooth-bore and with combustible cases in the Soviet 125mm smooth-bore gun in the T-64 MBTs.

The use of separate ammunition, by reducing the loading length of the round, enables a smaller turret ring to be employed, thereby making the tank smaller and lighter in addition to the other benefits, already mentioned, stemming from its use. The Soviet Army has carried the size and weight reduction further, in the case of the T-64 and T-72 tanks, by dispensing with the human loader in the turret and substituting an automatic loader of ingenious design to load the 125mm smooth-bore main armament. In the T-62 tank, mounting the 115mm smooth-bore gun, turret volume is reduced by ejecting the spent cartridge cases automatically from the turret.

All modern high-velocity tank guns, whether rifled or smooth-bore, incorporate the fume extractor or bore evacuator to prevent the propellant gases being sucked back into the fighting compartment as the breech opens after firing; this is indicated by the concentric cylindrical bulge about halfway down the barrel length.

The muzzle energy created by firing a modern high-velocity tank gun, which must be dissipated and absorbed by the recoil mechanism between the gun and its cradle, is very high for both rifled and smooth-bore guns; the recoil gear must not only slow the recoiling gun down to a stop before it can hit the back of the turret but it must also return it to its pre-firing position. To do this, the modern tank gun recoil gear usually consists of an hydraulic buffer mechanism to absorb the recoil, and an hydro-pneumatic recuperator system to return the gun to its normal position; the cylinders of these components are fixed to the cradle in which the gun slides, and the piston rods are attached to the gun. To absorb the energies involved they have to be large and heavy; mounted inside the turret, they add considerably to the volume swept by the elevating gun and thus to the volume requiring to be armoured. The gun cradle usually incorporates the gear that automatically opens the gun breech on recoil, as well as an indicator to show length of recoil, as a check on the state of the recoil gear.

The muzzle brake, with one or more baffles, mounted on the end of the gun barrel is a device formerly favoured by many tank gun designers as a means of reducing the size of the recoil gear required; it is not suitable for use with discarding sabot ammunition, however, being liable to damage from the sabot as it leaves the muzzle, and, as a consequence, is not now used for MBT main armament.

Since before the Second World War it has been the world-wide practice in tank turrets to mount a rifle calibre machine-gun coaxially with the main armament, which elevates and depresses with it, for the engagement of personnel at close range. This is the case with all current MBTs, many of which also carry a large calibre (12.7mm or 14.5mm) MG on an external mounting on top of the turret for anti-aircraft purposes, operated by the tank commander. In addition, most MBTs today carry externally mounted multi-barrelled smoke grenade-launchers on the turret front or side walls, which traverse with the turret and project a carefully calculated screen of close-range smoke over the frontal arc, to enable the tank to cover its movements.

Whereas prior to the Second World War the main armament tended to be shoulder-controlled in elevation, the wartime weights and out-of-balance of tank guns made manually controlled geared elevation essential. As stabilization of the main armament, first, in elevation (during the war) and later, also in azimuth (post-war) became a requirement, the need for powered elevation of the gun became obvious; by 1939 powered traverse of the turret had become essential due to the increase in weights, inertias and out-of-balance of the tank turrets of the time. Basically, three methods of powering traverse and elevation have been used: electric, electro-hydraulic and hydraulic; both electric and hydraulic systems were used in British

tanks during the war, but the greater vulnerability and flammability of hydraulic systems persuaded the British Army to use only electric systems in post-war tanks. That this was a correct decision has been shown by the great advances in electronics since the war, which mean that, nowadays, very compact, high-power, wide bandwidth, highly efficient solid-state electric drives can replace the much larger rotary electrical machines (metadynes) and hydraulic servos in new MBTs. The new drives 'chop' the vehicle's 28-volt supply up to 150V d.c. and control 150-volt servo-motors, which provide much more torque per amp than the existing 28-volt or 56-volt machines. Such drives are in the Brazilian Engesa tank Osorio, and will be fitted to the British Challenger.

The simple stabilization system first introduced in the wartime US M-4 Sherman replaced the earlier shoulder-controlled method of controlling the main armament in elevation only, so that it could, in theory, be fired with some accuracy when the tank was on the move. The idea revolved around a closed-loop servo-system, incorporating an electrically spun gyroscope to sense the angular velocities of the gun in elevation; any difference between these velocities and those commanded by the gunner via his elevation control caused the elevation servo-motor to rotate the gun in the opposite sense, thus nullifying the difference and stabilizing the gun in elevation. Although not very accurate, and needing some time for the gyroscope to warm up after switching the system on, it performed satisfactorily enough to convince the British and the Russian Armies, but not the US, of the value of a stabilization system in future native tank designs; in the case of the British, the system chosen for the post-war Centurion and its successors, the Chieftain and Challenger, was an all-electric one, stabilizing the main gun and coaxial MG in elevation and the whole turret in azimuth. With a two-axis system such as this, if the gunner holds his controls steady the stabilization system will maintain the position of the gun at a fixed bearing in space despite any movement of the vehicle in roll, pitch or yaw.

The Russians at first chose a simple electro-hydraulic elevation-only system, fitted in the early 1950s to the T-54/55 series, but changed to an azimuth and elevation system for subsequent MBTs. Full stabilization of turret and main and coaxial armament became standard in main battle tanks throughout the world, but, as turret weights and out-of-balance increased, as well as cross-country speeds, it became increasingly difficult to control gun and turret accurately on the move and required large and powerful systems to do so.

With the advent of the German Leopard 2 and later tanks elsewhere, however, a refinement of the system has been made; in this system, only the gunner's periscopic sight head is fully stabilized and the turret and armament are electronically 'slaved' to it, and can be brought into line with it automatically. The fire control system generates a stabilized aiming point in the gunner's sight and the gun fires only on coincidence, that is, when the gun bore is correctly aligned with the sight allowing for range and target movement. It is obviously much easier to stabilize accurately a small object such as a periscope mirror than one as large and heavy as a tank turret and takes very much less power to do so. The advent of ring laser gyros with no moving parts, in place of the older mechanically spinning type, will eliminate the need for a warming-up period on start-up as well as giving a more accurate and robust product, better able to withstand the harsh tank environment.

Mention of sights brings us to the question of visibility from tanks in general and fire control in particular. The best vision in a tank has always been accorded to the commander, who obviously needs to have good all-round vision to enable him to carry out his tactical task. This has usually meant his being

▶ A Chieftain tank with 'Still-brew' appliqué turret armour, showing clearly the screen wipers on the sight heads and the near IR spotlight and head-lamps. The main IR searchlight is contained in the box on the left side of the turret. (HQ 1(BR) Corps)

placed in the highest part of the tank, with his head out of the top in order that he can bring his binoculars to bear on any potential target or obstacle. In the earliest tanks, when it was necessary for him to 'close down' under fire, he used the vision slits provided in the armour of his cupola in order that he could still have reasonably all-round vision; the other crew members, who did not have the facility for having their heads outside the armour but who all played their part in all-round observation, were also provided with vision slits or ports, through which they could both see and bring their weapons to bear. It did not take the enemy long to realize, however, that the vision slits of tanks were good targets at which to fire, and the resulting injuries

to tank crews from lead 'splash' from hits and near misses on vision slits persuaded tank designers that some form of protection needed to be incorporated to reduce or prevent such injuries. Visors and chain mail masks did little to alleviate the problem, so thick glass blocks, placed behind the slits, were introduced; these were effective against bullet splash, but their light transmission was poor, reducing efficiency in conditions of poor light, and injuries from shattered glass were almost as numerous as those from bullet splash. By the end of the First World War it had been realized that it was best to remove the crewmen's eyes from the bullet or fragment path by bending the optical path of the vision device; this was done in all British tanks after the Mark IV by the use of periscopes, with all-round traverse and considerable movement in elevation, which could be changed, when damaged, from inside the tank.

Between the wars, periscopes were employed in virtually all tanks for crew members other than the driver, who continued to use glass blocks. As armour thicknesses increased during the Second World War, the provision of holes in the armour not only became more difficult but also reduced its resistance to attack; for observation, therefore, the commander was provided with a cupola giving all-round vision by means of either fixed replaceable episcopes in its walls or in a rotatable section of the turret roof. Drivers were given episcopes or rotating periscopes in the roof of the driver's compartment, as well as slits in the front plate, and the loader and gunner had a single periscope and the sight, respectively. By the end of the war, however, no form of opening in the frontal armour, meant to be the most invulnerable part of the tank, was permitted and periscopes only were provided for use by the driver when closed down; some form of seat mechanism was usually provided, however, to enable the driver to drive with his head out when out of contact with the enemy.

As the vision devices for other crew members were refined and reduced in number, as they increased in capability, those for the gunner involving the tank gun sighting systems became more and more complex; the open sights of the first tanks were soon replaced by simple straight tube telescopes, and these remained the standard between the wars and during the first part of the Second World War. The straight tube telescope, however, is just what it says, a straight tube containing a system of lenses and an aiming mark or cross-wires, mounted beside the main armament and elevating with

◄ A driver's image intensifier (II) driving periscope. Both eyepieces use a single object lens, which can be seen in the picture; such an instrument is known as bi-ocular, as opposed to binocular instruments which have an object lens for each eyepiece. (Pilkington PE Ltd.)

► A gunner's sighting telescope, in this case for the Soviet T-Series tanks. It incorporates a laser rangefinder and an optical and mechanical hinge, so that the eyepiece remains stationary when the gun is depressed or elevated. (Avimo Ltd.)

it, which required a hole in the gun mantlet armour to enable the gunner to see to aim the gun. He was thus vulnerable to a lucky enemy shot through the hole in the armour and had to move his head up and down as the gun was elevated or depressed. These problems were both overcome by the Germans, who had probably the best optical industry in Europe at that time, by incorporating an optical hinge in the telescope; this enabled the eyepiece to remain stationary while the object lens moved up and down with the gun, and, at the same time, enabled a piece of armour plate to be inserted in the sight line at the hinge, to prevent bullet or fragment penetration through the sight. So successful was this type of sight that the Russians copied it for their post-war range of tanks; it is particularly suitable for use with guns stabilized in elevation, as it obviates the need for the gunner to move his head up and down

to accommodate the random and sometimes very large movements of the straight tube telescope eyepiece as it moves with the gun.

The British, Americans and other tank-producing nations opted for another solution to the vulnerability and head movement problems posed by the straight tube telescopic sight; they eliminated altogether the need for having a potentially vulnerable hole in the armour of the gun mantlet by going to a periscopic sight, mounted in the turret roof and connected by linkage to the gun cradle, and, by doing so, also reduced the gunner's head movement by changing from an up and down to a much smaller backwards and forwards eyepiece movement. The periscope, as well as containing a vertically mounted telescope within its casing for gun sighting, also enabled the gunner to have a much wider observational

field of view. A drawback to the periscopic sight, of course, is the linkage connecting it to the gun cradle; expansion in high temperatures and contraction in low can play havoc with the sight/gun bore relationship, which ideally should be fixed for greatest accuracy, and complicated compensating devices have been developed to reduce this source of error.

There are many potential sources of error in the MBT sight/gun/ammunition relationship, of which the greatest in the past has been the measurement of range to the target. This obviously has a greater effect at the lower muzzle velocities and the higher trajectories, but even with the relatively flat trajectories of the high-velocity kinetic energy rounds, a small error in range estimation at the longer ranges can make all the difference between a hit and a near miss. Originally, the only method of obtaining the range to the target was by estimation, and various methods of doing this by relating the size of the target to objects of known dimensions at known ranges were tried; the simplest was the stadiametric method, in which tank outlines at typical fighting ranges were included in the sight pattern, the gunner having only to fit the target to the outline for the correct tangent elevation to be applied to the gun. This gave a marginally more accurate estimation than guesswork by the commander, but was still nowhere near accurate enough to ensure that the correct range was applied at all times; it was, however, the only available alternative to guesswork for some twenty years after the end of the Second World War.

In the later Marks of Centurion and in the Chieftain,

► A gunner's sighting periscope, this time for the Chieftain MBT. (Barr & Stroud Ltd.)

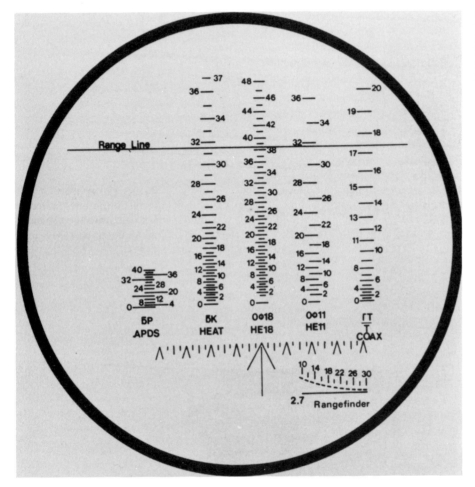

the British introduced the ranging MG as a means of
more accurately obtaining the range to a target; this
was a 0.5in (12.7mm) MG, mounted coaxially with the
main armament and ballistically matched to it as far
as possible, from which three bursts, each of three
tracer rounds, were fired in quick succession, one
short, one long and one at the target. The main gun
was then fired at this range, with a greatly increased
chance of a first-round hit. This method obviated the
need to waste scarce main armament rounds on the
straddling technique, and gave the enemy less indication that he was observed and under attack. No other
countries employed this method of range estimation.
The Germans with their excellent optical industry, still
favoured the use of optical instruments to solve the
range estimation problem; despite its requirement for

the user to have good binocular vision, they particularly favoured the stereoscopic rangefinder, mounting
it across the front of the turret to give it an adequate
optical base line. They later combined it with a
coincidence rangefinder, in which two images must be
moved into coincidence in the eyepiece to obtain the
range to the target. Such instruments are, however,
delicate and prone to variation with temperature;
accuracy was not greatly improved by their use, and it
was not until the invention and development of the
laser, an acronym for Light Amplification by Stimulated Emission of Radiation, that the range estimation
problem for main battle tanks and many other
weapons was solved. The laser rangefinder operates by
transmitting a single pulse of laser energy at the target;
this is reflected back from the target and detected by

the rangefinder receiver; the time between transmitting the pulse and receiving the returned signal is accurately measured, and permits the target range to be calculated with great accuracy. Today, the sighting systems of most of the world's MBTs incorporate laser rangefinders, accurate to 10 metres over ranges from 200 to 10,000 metres; unlike the early rangefinders based on ruby lasers, present ones employ lasers of Neodymium Glass (Nd YAG) which are safe to the human eye and have a better performance in mist and smoke. Carbon Dioxide (CO_2) lasers, which operate in the far infra-red part of the spectrum used by thermal imagers (*see below*) and have a very much improved ranging performance in poor visibility, are currently coming into service. Range is normally indicated digitally in metres in the gunner's sight field of view; it can also be applied automatically to the aiming mark, via the fire control computer or directly, so that the gunner merely has to lay the aiming mark on the target and fire.

With the virtual elimination of range error from the tank fire control system, other sources of error inherent in the system, formerly masked by the very much greater one of range estimation, came to prominence; and, as these were solved in their turn, others, the existence of which had not previously been considered, came to light. These can be broadly classified under the headings of:

1. Mechanical
2. Meteorological.
3. Ammunition
4. Tank attitude.

Sources of mechanical error can include backlash in the gun-laying mechanisms, temperature-induced variations in gun and gun/sight linkage, backlash in the gun/sight linkage, incorrect alignment of the sight with the gun, and gun wear. Meteorological conditions can cause gun barrel bend, variation in charge temperature with consequential variations in muzzle velocity, changes in projectile trajectory due to cross-wind between the gun and the target and due to variations in air density. Variations in charge and projectile weight can cause variations in muzzle velocity and trajectory of the projectile, while changes in tank attitude in the firing position, such as a side slope, inducting tilt of the gun trunnions, can adversely affect the relationship between the sight aiming mark and the point of strike of the projectile.

Most of these errors are individually small, but can be cumulatively large if corrective action is not taken.

In modern MBTs, the mechanical sources of error are countered by the use of compensated sight linkages or linkages that are not temperature sensitive, the incorporation of anti-backlash devices in elevation and traverse systems and the accurate recording of the number of rounds of each type fired through the gun to assess the state of barrel wear. To reduce barrel bend to a minimum, modern tank gun barrels are covered with a heat-insulating thermal sleeve to prevent differential heating and cooling by cold rain or wind upon a hot barrel; to make it insignificant as far as the coincidence of barrel axis and point of aim is concerned, modern tank gun barrels incorporate at the muzzle end an armoured housing containing a mirror, which reflects the aiming mark back into the gunner's sight. This muzzle reflector sight thus takes into account and nullifies all variable errors arising between the sight line and the axis of the bore, including bending of the gun barrel in any direction.

To take account of other errors, due to meteorological and other factors, modern MBT fire control systems incorporate sensors to sense cross-wind direction and speed, charge temperature in the stowage bins, air density and trunnion tilt. The outputs from these sensors are fed into an on-board digital fire control computer, which also takes into account the speeds of the target and its own tank, the number of rounds fired through the gun barrel and, hence, its state of wear, and the range to the target as fed into it by the laser rangefinder; the computer will calculate where the point of aim should be, taking into account all these variables, and will generate an aiming mark in the gunner's sight as well as automatically controlling the servos to move the turret and gun to the correct azimuth and elevation. In the Chieftain or Challenger, this process takes some 10 seconds. Typically, the computer information is fed also to the commander, who can also, if desired, override the gunner's controls to bring the gunner on to another target, or lay the gun and fire it himself.

Such systems are costly, and form a large part of the increased proportion of a modern MBT's total cost taken up by its electronics; other costly items are the optronic systems now considered essential for fighting and moving at night. Until well into the Second World War, it was not considered feasible for tanks to fight at night except in an emergency; even movement at night was difficult without lights, particularly across country. The human eye is sensitive only to a limited range of wavelengths in the electro-magnetic spectrum, and light of these wavelengths is limited even on the brightest moonlit night; on a dark night it is virtually blind, a condition made worse by attempting to see through a tank's vision devices.

During the later stages of the Second World War, both the Germans and the Western Allies made use of the near infra-red wavelengths to enable them to see to fight, to a limited extent, in the dark; in these systems, the target or the route to be traversed was illuminated in invisible (to the unassisted human eye) light from searchlights or headlights equipped with special dark filters, which allowed only light in the near infra-red wavelengths to pass; the target or route was then viewed through a special viewer which converted the near infra-red image to visible light. The range and resolution of these devices was very limited, but they did give the possessor of the equipment an advantage in the dark over an enemy without it; to an enemy also possessing it, however, the light from the searchlights or headlights indicated enemy target locations, and the vehicles carrying them were easy targets. The biggest disadvantage of the near infra-red systems was the fact that they were active, radiating light in large quantities, visible to an enemy passively viewing the scene through an IR viewing device. As, by the 1960s, most armies in the world had some form of near IR viewing equipment in service, the need for some other, passive, night vision system became urgent.

Luckily, several possibilities were by this time in development, the first to reach fruition and be taken into service being the Image Intensifier (II); this is a device that operates in the visible spectrum by amplifying, many tens of thousands of times, the visible light emanating from the stars even on the darkest night, making the night scene as visible as it would be by daylight. Completely passive in operation, it is in service with many armoured forces in the form of driving or observation binoculars, hand-held or head-mounted gun sights or static tripod-mounted long-range observation devices. It has, however, two disadvantages. First, because it operates in the visible light spectrum it suffers from one of the disadvantages of the unassisted human eye in being unable to see through fog, smoke and heavy rain. Secondly, again like the human eye losing dark adaptation in bright light, it is easily dazzled by gun flashes, tracer, burning houses or vehicles and laser light, and remains blinded for a short time after exposure. The image intensifier

is nevertheless a very useful device, likely to remain in service for several years for certain applications.

Another passive method of seeing in the dark employs Low Light Level Television (LLTV). The advantages of this system over the image intensifier are that the technology is relatively simple, and that the image can be transmitted from the camera, which can be located in the best observation position, by cable to remote viewing screens at any or all of the crew positions. Viewing a screen is less fatiguing for the crew member than keeping his face against the padded rubber eyepiece of an II sight or viewer; the tunnel vision effect of using an II or near IR viewer can be obviated with LLTV by giving the camera interchangeable or zoom lenses, so that the field of view can be changed when required. LLTV has the advantage that it can be made to operate in either the visible light, the near IR or the far IR parts of the electro-magnetic spectrum by merely changing the camera detector tube.

The presence of a target can be revealed either by the energy it reflects, when illuminated by a natural or an artificial source of radiation, or by the energy it emits, in the form of heat, light, sound or some other characteristic emission. Reflection of natural radiation from the sun by the target is used by normal daylight optical instruments; reflection of radiation by the stars at night is used by both image intensifiers and low light level TV. All these methods of target location are passive in operation, which are to be preferred to active ones since they do not require the target to be illuminated artificially; because they do not emit any radiation, they do not reveal the position of the observer and they consume less power, and are less bulky, than comparable active systems. However, the limitations of both image intensifiers and low light level TV in rain, fog and smoke, and the difficulties caused by sudden light sources in the field of view, meant that some other passive method of seeing in the dark was required. The obvious preference was for a system that would detect the energy emitted by the target, thus making detection independent of ambient light level.

Such a system is the thermal imager, enabling a target to be detected and recognized by the heat that it radiates. Heat radiation at certain wavelengths will penetrate mist, smoke and light foliage and is equally detectable in daylight or the darkest night; heat detection systems such as thermal imaging are therefore completely passive in operation, and can detect targets concealed to visual surveillance. The thermal imager operates in the 7.5–13 micron wavelength band of the electro-magnetic spectrum, and converts the heat radiated by the scene to a pictorial display resembling a conventional television picture. It uses a camera-lens system similar to a TV camera, the detector of which is cooled to the temperature of liquid nitrogen; this enabled low temperature differences as small as 0.5°C in the scene to be detected and to give adequate resolution in the resulting image to enable targets to be distinguished. In the image, which is monochrome, hot parts can be made to appear light and cold parts dark, or vice versa, according to preference.

The great advantage of the thermal imager, however, is that it works as well in daylight as in darkness; it can therefore penetrate camouflage, a man or vehicle concealed behind netting or vegetation standing out as a sharply defined and easily recognizable heat pattern. This facility means that thermal as well as mere optical camouflage will be needed in future wars and this thermal camouflage will have to duplicate nature's thermal patterns; attempts to mask a vehicle's or a man's heat signature will result in unnatural 'black holes' appearing in the scene, which will attract the attention of the observer as much as a target itself. The advent of the thermal imager has changed the character of warfare; no longer will darkness be the soldier's friend, giving him time to rest, recharge his batteries, feed, and maintain his weapons and vehicles, but it will be as a continuation of daylight, with every move and location observed, unless and until some satisfactory and easy means of thermally camouflaging men, weapons and vehicles is developed. Thermal imagers are costly, as are the means of supplying liquid nitrogen in the field, so that current AFV systems are limited to gunners; the US M-1 Abrams and the West German Leopard 2 are so equipped, and the Challenger is in the process of being so, while future system modifications will include the provision of individual thermal imaging devices for tank commanders and drivers, to replace the present image intensification devices. No doubt the Soviet Union and other Warsaw

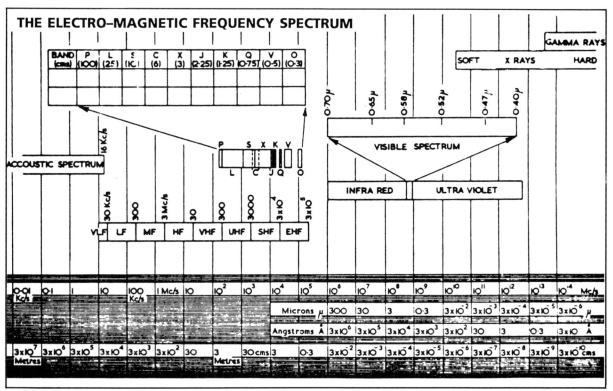

THE ELECTRO–MAGNETIC FREQUENCY SPECTRUM

A photograph of a thermal image of tank crews standing near their tanks. In this case, warm parts of the picture are white and cool parts black, but if desired this can be reversed on the viewing screen at the touch of a switch. (British Aerospace)

Pact countries are providing similar equipment for their MBT fleets, as well as reconnaissance units, infantry and helicopters.

In optronics, as in electronics, technology is developing rapidly, and new detector materials, production methods and techniques to improve the performance and picture quality of the thermal imager are already under development. One of the most promising developments, which can so improve detector sensitivity as to enable it to detect temperature differences as small as 0.1°C instead of the present 0.5°C, is the focal plane array. Another promising technique is to feed the outputs of different sensors into a computer and to use artificial intelligence techniques to compare the images created and distinguish targets automatically. Application of these and other techniques lies in the future, however; for the present, the thermal imager represents the best available target location system, by day or night.

The firepower of the main battle tank has been discussed at length, but little has so far been said about the other armoured fighting vehicles in an army's equipment inventory. This is because the MBT is a so much more complex and sophisticated piece of equipment, and its firepower so much more devastating,

than any other AFV that, by comparison, the other AFVs seem pale and uninteresting; also, if one has a grasp of the problems encountered in designing and using a tank's firepower it will be no problem to understand the very much simpler firepower of the armoured car, light tracked reconnaissance vehicle and infantry fighting vehicle. The first two of these categories have been with us since the First World War; in fact, the armoured car, as we have seen, was the first armoured and armed vehicle to enter service on either side during that war. The infantry fighting vehicle, on the other hand, has made its appearance only in the 1970s, although the concept has been with us rather longer, but in none of these three categories of vehicle is firepower rated highly; in fact, in each case it is rated below both protection and mobility. In the IFV, protection and mobility are rated equal first priority, while in the other two categories mobility is the most important characteristic.

There is little, therefore, to add to what has already been said about the MBT's firepower when discussing that of armoured cars, light tracked reconnaissance vehicles and infantry fighting vehicles. All carry smaller calibre main armament, ranging from 25–30mm automatic cannon, firing both kinetic and chemical energy projectiles, to 73–90mm low-velocity, low-recoil energy guns, firing chemical energy projectiles only; these guns are all turret-mounted, with a coaxial small calibre MG and with 360° traverse. Guns are usually manually elevated but traversed by power; most are without stabilization, and are therefore unable to fire on the move. Some IFVs, notably the Soviet BMP-1 and -2 and the American M-2 and M-3 Bradley vehicles, however, are the exception in mounting anti-tank missile-launchers, for long-range engagement of enemy armour, as well as the gun main armament. The M-2 and M-3 differ also in having all-electric stabilization systems for their turrets and guns.

Sighting systems in these categories of AFV are simpler than those of the MBT, and night vision devices tend to be of the image intensification type on NATO infantry combat vehicles; Warsaw Pact vehicles tend to rely on near IR, using filtered headlamps and searchlights for illumination. Reconnaissance vehicles, on the other hand, require the most sophisticated devices available if they are to carry out their task properly. Some reconnaissance vehicles are equipped with battlefield surveillance radar; although an active system, this type of radar can detect movement through rain and IR-opaque smoke and therefore has an advantage over the thermal imager, in this connection only. As an active system radar is, of course, vulnerable to all the tricks of electronic warfare, such as missiles that home on to electro-magnetic emissions, jammers and decoys, and this places limitations on its battlefield usefulness.

Having summarized the development of tank firepower from the first prototype of 1916 up to the main battle tanks of today, we must now make an attempt to foresee the lines along which it might further develop after the turn of the century. The obvious point that the armament of a tank is dependent on its role was made at the beginning of this chapter, but even assuming that the future role of the MBT were to remain the same as that of today's tanks there are many ways in which the performance of its armament could be improved, these improvements being applicable to most possible roles.

There are two main alternatives for the main armament of a main battle tank, the guided missile or the gun. The gun is unlikely to be displaced as tank main armament by a guided missile, however, for two main reasons: first, the longer time of flight and lower rate of fire of the guided missile make it more difficult to

use in developing tactical situations and, secondly, its inability to use kinetic energy attack limits its usefulness against armour. The task of the enemy tank designer is made much easier if he has only one type of attack to counter, and chemical energy attack can be defeated by the use of composite and reactive armour. Missiles have their place in the attack of armour, notably with the attack helicopter and the infantry, both of which require a launcher with no recoil which can employ large shaped-charge cone diameters. The gun can fire both kinetic and chemical energy rounds, and the latter can vary from HEAT and HESH for the attack of armour to HE and case shot for the attack of personnel, emplacements and helicopters, and to smoke for blinding the enemy. The gun is a 'fire and forget' weapon, with a high rate of fire, a medium range and pin-point accuracy.

It seems probable that all future tank guns will be smooth-bore rather than rifled; even in the current generation of MBTs, the only NATO or Warsaw Pact country to persist with rifled guns is Great Britain. The smooth-bore gun has many advantages over a rifled one. High-energy propellants, which cause excessive barrel wear when used with the driving bands of spin-stabilized projectiles in rifled barrels, can be employed, thus giving higher muzzle velocities. The chrome plating of the bore adheres very much better to a smooth-bore than to a rifled one, thus also having a beneficial effect on barrel wear. Lastly, it is possible to fire fin-stabilized projectiles without the complication and additional friction losses of a slipping driving band; APDS high-velocity KE projectiles can be given a greatly enhanced penetration performance if the cross-sectional density of the penetrator can be increased by increasing its length beyond the limit imposed by spin-stabilization. We have already seen that the performance of HEAT ammunition is degraded by spinning the projectile, so here too the smooth-bore gun scores. It is likely, therefore, that the UK will convert to smooth-bore and thus restore the NATO standardization in tank gun ammunition last attained with the 105mm tank gun.

The gun has several disadvantages, however, some of which were touched upon earlier in this chapter. One disadvantage is the length and weight of its ammunition, both of which have so increased, in calibres above 105mm, that separate loading of charge and projectile and auto-loading have had to be resorted to. Projectiles are essential, but are the present forms of charge the most economical way in which to propel them up a gun barrel? The bagged charge of Challenger has the advantage of being totally consumed in the breech on firing, while the semi-combustible cartridge of the smooth-bore 120mm gun mounted in Leopard 2, Leclerc and Abrams leaves only the metal cartridge base to be ejected after firing; both are, however, bulky and rigid. Brass cartridge cases, as used in the Soviet T-72, form a considerable additional fire hazard if they are penetrated by fragments, as well as adding weight; they also take up much space in the turret after firing and until they can be disposed of, although the Soviet T-72 solves this problem by automatically ejecting the case from the turret after firing. In addition to the propellant, the primers which initiate it when the gunner presses his firing button require stowage space; in the cased or semi-cased round, the primer, usually initiated electrically, is incorporated in the base of the cartridge case and requires no additional stowage space. This is true, for example, of the US/German separate ammunition for their 120mm smooth-bore tank gun, in which the primer is incorporated in the stub case and ejected with it after firing. With bagged charge separate ammunition, however, such as is fired from the British Chieftain and Challenger 120mm rifled gun, primers (or vent tubes as the British Army calls them) are separate components and must be loaded separately into the breech; rather like rifle blank cartridges, they are contained in a magazine, mounted on the gun's breech.

Various ways of dealing with the ammunition loading and stowage problem are currently being investigated in Western countries and the Soviet Union. The least radical proposal is to dispense with the human loader in the turret, thereby allowing the lowering of both the turret roof and the vehicle height, and replacing him with a mechanical auto-loader. Both the Soviet MBTs T-64 and T-72 already incorporate auto-loaders; in the T-64, the projectile is stowed vertically beside the propellant, with the disadvantage that the projectile has to be turned to the horizontal before it can be rammed. In the T-72, however, the projectile is stowed horizontally, below the charge, in a box up to 40 of which are stowed in a carousel below the turret basket; once the tank commander has selected the nature of ammunition he wishes to fire, the carousel is then raised until the projectile is level with the breech and the projectile is rammed home by a swing arm; after ramming of the projectile, the box is lowered

slightly to allow the charge to be rammed. A drawback to auto-loading systems generally is that, to load, the gun must be returned to a pre-set elevation datum position, in the case of the T-72 an elevation of 4°; its designers claim that a rate of fire of 8 to 10 rounds per minute can be attained despite this requirement, although other agencies claim that problems have been encountered with the auto-loader, which limit the actual rate of fire obtainable to 3 to 4 rounds per minute. The French, on the other hand, feel that the auto-loader to be provided in the Leclerc will increase the rate of fire by facilitating the handling of the large, fixed 120mm rounds used in this tank. In this case, the auto-loader and the ammunition itself are stowed in the turret 'bustle' behind the gun. Auto-loading forms part of feasibility studies of possible future tank configurations currently being carried out in the USA, UK and West Germany; these are also investigating such radical options as mounting the gun externally and dispensing with the conventional turret, reducing crew numbers and locating them in the hull and the remote operation and laying of the armament, with a view to reducing both vehicle weight, by reducing armoured volume, cost and the target presented to enemy fire.

To revert to the theme mentioned earlier, how much easier the auto-loading problem would be if the conventional propellant charge could be dispensed with, leaving only the projectile to be dealt with by a mechanical handling device; how much easier also the stowage of the charges would be if they could be made flexible, to fit in otherwise unused space in the tank. Two possible approaches to the solution of these problems have been suggested, both of which have been proved in theory in the past, but which awaited development of the associated technology before becoming practical propositions.

The first approach involves the use of liquid propellants (LP) instead of solids. In theory, the injection and ignition of a precisely metered quantity of a suitable liquid explosive in the breech of a gun should be as effective as conventional solid propellant in accelerating the projectile; if this proved to be so, the employment of liquid propellant would have many advantages:

1. There would be no cartridge case to be ejected and disposed of, as with fixed ammunition, and no unburnt residue in the chamber, as with combustible-cased ammunition.

2. Only the projectiles would need to be stowed in the fighting compartment near to the gun; propellant liquid could be stowed remotely from the gun, in a safer location in, or even outside, the vehicle.
3. Logistic benefits would accrue with regard to storage, transport and loading into the tank.
4. Financial savings could be expected in the ammunition manufacturing process.
5. For a given number of rounds, weight would be reduced.
6. For a given weight of projectile, LP should give a 10 per cent increase in MV.
7. Better use made of vehicle internal volume.
8. Reduced muzzle flash.

Much research into LP guns has been carried out in the UK, West Germany and USA, particularly in the latter as an outgrowth of rocket liquid propellant technology. In 1987, the US Congress set aside funds for a liquid propellant tank gun programme based on a 120mm smooth-bore gun suitable for installation in the M-1 Abrams. The British ultimate goal is also a 120mm LP tank gun, but their research programme and that of the West Germans is some five years behind that of the USA. Several possible propellants have been studied, of both single (mono-propellant) and double (bi-propellant) component types; mono-propellants consist of only one liquid, while bi-propellants are made up of two, the fuel and the oxidant, which are stored and fed to the gun separately. The advantage of bi-propellants is that they are quite safe until mixed; their disadvantage, that they require two separate storage tanks, pipework, pumps and injector systems.

Current US and British research is concentrated on mono-propellant systems, that of West Germany on both mono- and bi-propellants. The preferred mono-propellant is based on Hydroxyl Ammonium Nitrate (HAN); it is water-based and does not decompose rapidly as some other propellants do. Apart from choice of propellant, problems have arisen in the injection and pump system; it is obviously essential to have a precisely metered amount of propellant injected every time, in order to maintain accuracy of fire and consistency of ballistics from round to round, and in the early experiments this was difficult to achieve. Sealing of the gun breech after the projectile has been loaded has also proved difficult, but these and other problems have been overcome to the extent that the US prototype, a 155mm vehicle-mounted artillery howitzer, is due to give a 'proof of principle' firing

demonstration at the US Artillery School at Fort Sill in 1991. At this rate a viable LP tank gun is likely to be available by the turn of the century, and would seem to be the most likely tank armament of the foreseeable future. The use of liquid propellant rather than conventional solid propellant charges would make the loading and operation of the externally mounted gun very much simpler.

Coupled with the use of liquid propellant will be new means of charge ignition. One promising method currently under test dispenses altogether with the conventional primer or vent tube, replacing it by laser energy. In this method, laser energy is piped through a fibre optic cable directly into the breech through a pressure window; this allows the breech design to be simplified, higher rates of fire, the possibility of higher muzzle velocities and the absence of disposable components such as the fired vent tube.

Another means of replacing the conventional solid propellant charge, although one very much more in the future than liquid propellant, is the electro-magnetic gun. The charge in this type of weapon is an electrical rather than a solid or a liquid one, and the US Strategic Defence Initiative (SDI) programme has revived interest in a principle, first put forward in experimental form in 1845, for accelerating a projectile electrically rather than chemically. The muzzle velocities of existing high-performance guns are already near to both physical and technical limits, and these limits are likely to be reached in the next generation of tank guns, even using liquid propellants. The physical laws governing electro-magnetic propulsion of projectiles permit theoretical velocities greater than those of chemically propelled projectiles, and this is one of the main advantages of the electro-magnetic gun. Another advantage is its independence from raw materials and industrial capacity for conventional propellants, which could be crucial in a crisis. Cost of ammunition would be very much reduced, as only projectiles would need to be manufactured, stored, transported and stowed in vehicles. An electro-magnetic gun would be more survivable than a conventional gun system and, without the load of chemical propellant, a tank's flammability in the event of an armour penetration would be greatly reduced.

With all these advantages accruing from its use, it is perhaps surprising that the electro-magnetic gun did not replace the conventional gun many years ago; the simple answer is that the lack, until recently, of a suitable means of storing the electrical energy involved hindered its realization. Recent developments in electronics, however, should lead to considerable progress in electrical energy storage, thus increasing the feasibility of weapon systems employing electro-magnetic guns.

Three basic types of electro-magnetic gun have so far been proposed and tried experimentally: the coil gun, the rail gun and the electro-thermal gun. In the first type, the gun consists of a barrel containing a series of fixed acceleration coils at intervals down its length; the projectile also carries a coil around its circumference. When the barrel coils are electrified in sequence, the travelling magnetic field induces acceleration in the projectile. The rail gun, as its name suggests, consists of two parallel rails in place of the barrel, the projectile gliding between them; when an electric current source is connected to the rails, the current flows through one rail to the projectile, then back in the other direction through the other rail, creating a force on the current flowing through the armature of the projectile and thus accelerating it. First patented by a Frenchman in 1920, several spectacular tests of the rail gun have taken place both in the USA and the USSR since the Second World War, very high projectile velocities having been attained. The electro-thermal gun in its simplest form consists of a conventional gun barrel with electrodes leading to a plasma burner mounted on the breech end of the weapon; a voltage passed across the plasma burner's electrodes creates an arc that vaporizes material, such as polyethylene, situated between the electrodes. The vaporized material is super-heated until it becomes a high-pressure plasma, which accelerates the projectile up the bore. Tests conducted in the 1960s showed that electro-magnetic guns can achieve higher muzzle velocities than conventional guns, but, due to the lack at that time of suitable power sources, the muzzle energies necessary for weapon applications were unable to be reached.

Since then, developments have progressed steadily; work on all critical components of the electro-magnetic gun is proceeding rapidly in the USA and probably also in the USSR, and is beginning in other countries as well. Progress so far with regard to the accelerator, energy storage and impulse formation makes it appear probable that some weapon systems after the turn of the century will begin to be equipped with electro-magnetic guns; in view of its self-contained power source and its cross-country load-carrying capacity,

the tank would seem to be a most likely recipient of such a weapon system.

As gun muzzle velocities increase and projectile trajectories become flatter, great accuracy in gun and fire control systems will be required in the future. Stabilization systems to enable accurate fire across country on the move will continue to be needed, and the best method will probably continue to employ fully stabilized sights, with the weapon slaved to them and firing on coincidence. The commander and gunner will continue to require 'top vision' in order to have the best observation, and this is likely to be best given by remote sensor heads located beside or above the gun giving both night and day vision of high resolution, with variable magnification and field of view. These can be connected to the crew stations via an 'optical slip ring' and possibly integrated with automatic target identification, automatic tracking and miss-distance sensing, as well as the necessary ranging system.

The development of 'smart' target-seeking and self-guiding projectiles for tank guns, to allow top attack of armoured targets and attack helicopters is also likely; these will, of course, require lower muzzle velocities than the kinetic energy projectiles, if only to protect their sensitive guidance and fuzing systems.

The detection and attack of of attack helicopters will become one of the tank crew's biggest problems in any future war, and one to which considerably more attention than appears at present to be the case will need to be given. The introduction within armoured units of special vehicles equipped with aircraft detection and location systems and specialized gun/missile armament, will undoubtedly be necessary, but these can only be provided on a small scale of one per tank company or possibly per platoon/troop; more will need to be done to enable the ordinary MBT, whose armament elevation arc is more than adequate, to take on the attack helicopter and even the helicopter-launched missile with its main armament. The position at present is worst in the British Army, where a combination of cap-badge politics and financial stringency has prevented the development and introduction of both anti-aircraft tanks and anti-helicopter detection systems and projectiles for normal MBTs.

There are three problems here. The first is the ordinary ground-attack aircraft, armed with both guns and anti-tank missiles. For this role, specialized AA tanks are the answer, equipped with a (preferably passive) aircraft detection and location system with a missile/gun weapon system slaved to it. It must be stated, however, that no satisfactory passive method of both detecting and ranging an aircraft target exists at present, and radar homing missiles present a very real threat to the viability of present radar-based AA systems.

The second problem is the hovering, missile-armed helicopter, flying the nap-of-the-earth (NOTE); if this can be detected in time, before it can launch a missile, it is perfectly possible for the MBT to shoot it down with its direct fire main armament, provided that it has a suitable main armament projectile. It could do this with either its kinetic energy anti-armour projectile, although this would represent a considerable degree of overkill, or with its existing HE or HESH projectile, provided that a suitable proximity (VT) fuze were available, or with a specialized anti-helicopter projectile such as chain- or case-shot. The main problem here is detection of the helicopter by the tank; flying nap-of-the-earth and hovering to fire, the helicopter exposes very little of itself, and the tank, in any event, is likely to be looking for ground targets in an entirely different direction. Fortunately, however, the helicopter's rotors and sight must be above the obstacle behind which it is hiding, and a helicopter's rotors have a very distinctive heat signature. A possible detection system, therefore, might involve a horizontally and vertically scanning thermal detector, covering a vertical arc of, at the most, 5° above the horizon, and 360° in azimuth, which could alert the tank commander and to which the main armament could be slaved when required; at the minimum, the tank would require a proximity-fuzed HE or HESH round with which to engage the helicopter, and such a projectile is not currently in the armoured unit ammunition inventory. Better still might be a thermally or electronically fuzed case or chain-shot round, which would automatically explode in the proximity of, and ideally above, the helicopter, inflicting terminal damage on its rotors and engine.

The third problem is the already-launched helicopter missile; if launched from an already-detected helicopter, the missile might also be directly engaged with the main armament, whose projectile time of flight is very much less than that of the guided missile. Although a very small target, particularly at typically long missile ranges, the tank thermal sight should be able to pick up the missile's thermal emissions, particularly against a terrain background, and either a KE or a CE projectile should kill the missile if hit. An alternative to the thermal detector made possible by the distinctive audio signature of helicopters might be an acoustic detector and direction indicator; this should have the advantage of being cheaper than the thermal detection method, but would undoubtedly be less precise in operation.

The threat posed to armoured units by the stand-off helicopter has now reached such proportions that direct action by the MBT itself has become essential. Some form of detection and indication system will need to be provided for it, as well as one or more types of specialist anti-helicopter projectile, in addition to the specialist anti-aircraft tanks, which have, in the UK, yet to be developed and which can only be procured in relatively small quantities when they are developed.

In view of the importance and superiority over visible light systems of the thermal sighting and observation system of the modern MBT, considerable effort will undoubtedly, over the next few years, be devoted to methods of deceiving it. Thermal screening smoke is already with us, but there will be a plethora of devices designed to decoy it away from the real target, or to hide the target itself from detection and observation. Alternative heat sources will have to be backed up by effective camouflage in both far IR and visible spectra, although little has so far been published on this subject.

In the 21st century, therefore, we can expect to see the MBT armed with a hyper-velocity main armament, firing liquid-propelled projectiles loaded automatically; this main armament is likely to be mounted above the vehicle hull rather than in a turret as at present, together with the sighting, observation and detection sensors, whose images will be relayed to both commander and gunner, probably located in the hull. The armament will probably continue to be slaved to a fully stabilized sighting system, firing on coincidence, and the sighting system should incorporate some form of indicator of helicopter targets, probably based on a scanning thermal pointer or acoustic detector. The tank armament is most likely to continue to incorporate a coaxial small-calibre MG, as well as thermal/visible smoke grenade-dischargers.

A later development could well be an electromagnetic gun, to replace the LP main armament, but this is likely to be several years into the century, at least for tank use.

obility is the state of being mobile, which is itself defined, in Collins' National Dictionary, as 'capable of moving rapidly from place to place'. It is exactly this sense of the term which applies to its use in a military context, and particularly in connection with the characteristics of armoured fighting vehicles; these need to be able to move rapidly from place to place not only to enable their firepower to be used to best advantage but also to enhance the crews' protection by lessening the chances of being hit by enemy fire. In this latter application, 'mobility' is nowadays frequently coupled with 'agility', defined as 'speed of motion, nimbleness', in the statement of military requirements for a new AFV.

Mobility, as applied to an AFV, has two aspects:

1. *Strategic mobility*, the ability to move to, or between, theatres of war.
2. *Tactical mobility*, the ability to move within a theatre of war, and on the battlefield.

Limitations are imposed on AFV design by the requirement for the vehicle to have strategic mobility, which involves the ability to be transported by land, sea and, in some cases, air; these make themselves felt in the form of absolute and clear-cut restrictions on weight and size. The principal considerations may be summarized as follows:

1. *Length*. In general, maximum length is dictated more by technical than by transportation factors, such as steering ratio in the case of tracked, and turning radius in the case of wheeled vehicles.
2. *Width*. The restriction on movement imposed by width varies considerably between transport systems. The tightest restrictions generally applicable to AFVs are those imposed by the rail loading gauge. Generally speaking, if the rail limitations are met, there will be no problem in sea transport, but air transport restrictions vary from aircraft to aircraft and are generally too tight for any but the lightest AFVs.
3. *Height*. Again, the tightest restriction is generally that of the rail loading gauge. The 2.5m (8ft) limit imposed by aircraft cargo doors and compartments applies only to light AFVs.
4. *Cross Section*. In addition to the simple considerations of width and height, a vehicle may be further restricted by the height at which the maximum width occurs; this applies especially to movement by rail,

and is defined by the rail loading gauge.
5. *Weight*. Fifty to sixty tonnes is the normal limit for strategic movement, by rail, sea and land. Limit for movement by air depends upon the stage length, but 20 tonnes is the maximum acceptable, and that only for short stages.

For air movement, other restrictions may also apply. For example, equipment that may be carried in unpressurized aircraft must be designed to withstand the rapid changes in pressure associated with take-off and landing. The main problem areas here will be fuel tanks, hydraulic systems and pressurized or sealed compartments. Any equipment that may be carried by air must also be designed to withstand the high acceleration loads associated with this form of transportation; tie-down points must be provided, and vehicles with soft suspensions may require suspension locks.

Having met the dimensional and weight limitations imposed by the requirement for the vehicle to have strategic mobility, the designers of an AFV now have to work within these to design a vehicle whose in-built characteristics will give it the degree of tactical and battlefield mobility, and the agility, specified by the military user of the vehicle in his statement of requirements. On the battlefield, the route a vehicle takes is dictated largely by tactical considerations; it must therefore be able to take the tactically desirable route regardless of terrain, and to manoeuvre freely and speedily. The component parts of the vehicle that contribute directly to its mobility are the automotive and the running gear. The automotive part comprises the power plant, the means of transmitting the power to the wheels or tracks and the steering and braking systems, and, in tracked AFVs, is nowadays usually joined into one unit known as the power pack. The running gear consists of the road wheels, springing and damping (suspension) system and, in the case of a tracked vehicle, the tracks.

In addition to the dimensional and weight constraints inherent in strategic mobility, other limitations are imposed on the designers of an AFV by the laws of physics, and these must be met if the vehicle is to have acceptable tactical mobility. Among these, for tracked vehicles, is the relationship between the length of track on the ground and the width between the centres of the tracks, known as the L/C, or steering, ratio. Another, applying both to tracked and wheeled vehicles, is the ratio of vehicle laden weight to the area of track or wheels in contact with the ground, over which this weight is distributed, known as the nominal ground pressure and measured in lb/in^2 (or psi) or kN/m^2. A third, also applicable to both wheeled and tracked vehicles, is the ratio of power to vehicle weight, expressed in bhp/tonne or kW/kN.

It has been found by experience that, for maximum mobility, a tracked vehicle's steering ratio should lie between 1.2 and 1.7; anything below this minimum will result in the vehicle being directionally unstable, while anything above the maximum will make the vehicle almost impossible to turn. Nominal ground pressure (NGP) for tracked and wheeled vehicles should, for preference, be between 6 and 12 psi; anything less will result in the vehicle lacking adhesion on hard surfaces and slopes, anything more and it will bog down in soft going across country. Power to weight ratio should be not less than 15bhp/tonne (1.12kW/kN) to give a satisfactory performance; the greater the amount by which this minimum is exceeded, the better will be the mobility and agility of the vehicle. Ratios of more than 25bhp/tonne (1.87kW/kN) will give an excellent performance, while above 30bhp/tonne the speed and acceleration will be approaching that of the average private car.

These criteria have, however, only been learned the hard way since the first armoured cars and tanks appeared during the First World War. Although designed with the express purpose of restoring mobility to a static battlefield, the mobility of the early tanks was minimal. Admittedly they were designed to specific requirements which included the ability to cross wide trenches and to climb out of deep, steep-walled shell holes, and their maximum speed was purposely limited to the walking speed of the infantryman; nevertheless, they were highly unreliable, had poor soft ground performance and were grossly underpowered. These faults in the heavy tanks were recognized even before the end of the war and the faster, more agile 'Whippet' or medium tanks were designed with the purpose of exploiting the breakthroughs made by the heavy tanks, although they did not appear in action until March 1918. All the British heavy tanks weighed between 28 and 35 tons, but despite this weight their power plants had outputs of only 105bhp in the Mark I and 225bhp in the Mark V**, giving power/weight ratios of 3.75 and 6.4bhp/ton, respectively. The matter is put into perspective when one

remembers that many modern family cars have engines of greater output than these early tank engines. It must, however, be remembered that in 1915 the internal combustion engine had not long been perfected and it was only the invention of this type of prime mover that had enabled the dreams of many generations of soldiers to be fulfilled; a mobile carrier of firepower, with protection for its crew, not tied to the speed and pulling power of the horse.

It was not only the lack of suitably powerful power plants that limited the mobility of the first tanks. Tracks of suitable design were not available and had to be designed and developed virtually from scratch. That the poor design of track was largely responsible for the early tanks' poor mobility was shown when an experimental 'snake' track was tried on an otherwise standard Mark V tank, and succeeded in trebling its maximum speed to 12mph. All the British tanks of the First World War were unsprung, however, and the resulting ride was most uncomfortable for the crew, as well as imposing stresses and strains on the structure and components of the vehicles; any increase in the vehicle's speed capability would have resulted in it shaking itself to pieces.

Transmissions were also basic; in the early Marks of British heavy tank, gear-changing and steering were cumbersome and tiring operations, requiring two men to operate the gears, controlled by hand signals from the driver, and another to operate the brakes. In addition, the Mark I had a steering 'tail', consisting of two wheels on an hydraulically lifted frame; these wheels were connected to the driver's steering wheels, so that, in good going, the tank could be steered in a circle of about 60 metres radius without involving the gear-changers or brakeman. In the heavy going encountered in France, however, the tail wheels proved a complete failure; they were removed in November 1916, never to return as a means of steering.

The Mark V incorporated a much improved transmission and steering system, consisting of a 4-speed and reverse gearbox driving epicyclic steering boxes by means of a cross shaft, and incorporating pedal-operated brakes for each track. Gear changing and steering were thus greatly simplified; to turn the tank, the driver pulled one of the two steering levers, thereby releasing the sun pinion in the appropriate epicyclic gear and allowing it to idle without transmitting power. An acute turn could be made by means of the relevant pedal-operated track brake.

Other types of transmission were proposed, including petrol-electric, petrol/hydraulic and the Wilson epicyclic. The petrol/electric drive consisted of an electric generator for each track, driven by the tank engine; each generator powered an electric motor, which in turn drove the track sprocket. Speed was infinitely variable between limits, and steering was achieved by varying the speed on each track as necessary. Speed and steering were controlled by one man. The Williams-Janney petrol/hydraulic drive was similar in principle, substituting two sets of hydraulic pumps and motors for the electric generators and motors, one set to each track. With this system also, speed was infinitely variable within limits and this and steering could again be controlled by one man. These systems were rejected after a comparative trial in March 1917, however, as being too complicated, heavy and expensive for mass production in wartime; the Wilson epicyclic gearbox was chosen instead, and variations of this transmission were still in service in British AFVs until well after the Second World War.

The tanks of the First World War were, of course, special cases designed to meet a very specialized requirement, and their relevance to the design of subsequent tanks was really limited to the experience that had been gained by the military in the operation, and industry in the building, of track-laying vehicles. Once mobility had been restored to the battlefield, AFVs were required to maintain it by keeping up the momentum; obstacle-crossing became a subsidiary, rather than the primary aim, and speed of movement, especially across country, assumed greater importance. Ease of operation, and reliability, of the automotive components of mobility, such as power plant, transmission, steering and braking, became paramount as vehicle crews were reduced in number; to enable them to function properly at their destination, running gear components such as suspension, dampers, road wheels and tracks had to give a comfortable ride over all types of terrain, as well as an adequate life and standard of reliability in service. In order to understand the reasons for the choice of present systems and the probable course of future development, it is necessary for the reader to know the problems that have been encountered in the past and how they have been solved in today's AFVs. To do this, we will briefly summarize the trends in design of those automotive and running gear components affecting vehicle mobility between the First World War and the present.

The fundamental automotive component is, of course, the power plant and, as a result, the engine has always been a major element in tank development. The development devoted to piston engines over the years, and the wide choice of commercially available engines with either spark (internal combustion) or compression (diesel) ignition, have made the piston engine the normal choice for vehicles; in comparisons with other types, the piston engine is taken as the standard by which they are judged. The type and shape of tank engines were, for many years, dictated by commercial automotive practice and indeed by commercially available engines; as power outputs rose to give the increased power/weight ratios demanded by tank users, however, increasingly specialized engine designs were demanded. The engine has become the major component dictating the height of a tank's hull, and in the search for lower tank silhouettes, engine design plays a major part.

Between the world wars, the Soviet Union and Japan preferred diesel engines, while the rest of the world opted for spark ignition engines running on petrol. The stringencies of wartime, however, compelled both Britain and the USA to employ tank engines of both types, and the reduced fire hazard offered by diesel fuel (DERV) as compared to petrol has tempted many other countries since the Second World War to make the change, especially as the compression ignition engine offers some 40 per cent saving on fuel consumption. Compression ignition engines, however, tend to be heavier for a given power output than do those employing spark ignition, although using less fuel to cover a given distance; the greater the pressure to which the fuel/air mixture is compressed the greater the engine efficiency, and compression ignition engines generally have higher compression ratios than their spark ignition rivals. High compression ratios demand heavy construction, hence the greater specific weight of compression ignition engines.

All types of cylinder arrangement, including in-line, vee, X, radial and opposed piston, have been employed in the piston engines used in tanks; as power outputs rose, however, the in-line arrangement became too long for tank installation and the vee tended to take its place. The opposed piston arrangement, as used in the Chieftain tank's Leyland engine, permits a low hull roof in the horizontal layout, but cooling of this type of engine is more of a problem than with other types. Engine cooling is one of the greatest problems facing

▶ A typical MBT power pack, in this case for the Engesa Osorio MBT. It comprises a MWM water-cooled diesel engine of 1,040bhp output and the ZF LSG-3000 transmission. (Engesa)

the tank designer, and operation of the cooling fans can take between 10–20 per cent of the engine's power; air cooling tends to absorb more engine power than liquid cooling. Radiators for liquid-cooled engines occupy a large volume in the engine compartment and their location needs careful thought to allow access to the engine for maintenance.

As the weights of main battle tanks have risen since the end of the Second World War so the power of their engines has had to be constantly increased to give them the required power/weight ratio. As a result, the volume of the engine compartments of recent NATO MBTs has risen to 6–7 cubic metres, which represents some 35–40 per cent of the tanks' internal volume and accounts for much of their large size and weight. By comparison with their volume, however, the weights of the engines are much less important, taking on average only some 10 per cent of the tank's total weight; this is because the armour surrounding the large engine compartment is heavier than the propulsion system it contains, weighing some 1.5 tonnes for each cubic metre it surrounds. It is therefore a matter of urgency to the tank designer to find ways of reducing drastically

the volume occupied by modern power plants and their cooling systems. One step that has been taken by most designers of the latest MBTs is to integrate the engines, transmissions and cooling groups and tailor the result into a 'power pack' designed for a specific vehicle, removable from the tank, for maintenance or replacement, as a complete unit. Another has been to increase the power density of the engine compartment by increasing the output of the engine by supercharging it in one of various ways. Most modern tank engines are V-12 diesels; some, such as those of the West German Leopard 1 and the Soviet T-72, have been fitted with mechanically driven superchargers, while others such as those powering the German Leopard 2, the British Challenger and the US M-60 have been fitted with the thermally more efficient turbocharger.

Other approaches to the reduction of engine compartment volume and increased power density have been taken, notably by the US in their selection of a gas turbine to power their MBT, the M-1 Abrams. The gas turbine has many advantages as a tank power plant, among which are its small size and weight relative to its output, its smaller cooling requirement and its instant full power availability on start-up. Its disadvantages are its greater fuel consumption than diesel engines of comparable power, its greater cost and its sensitivity to dust in the air that it breathes, although all these are being worked on and improvements have already been achieved. It remains to be seen which will prove to be the better tank power plant in the future, especially as the advent of a viable gas turbine in the M-1 is spurring the diesel engine designers and producers on to methods of reducing the cooling requirements and increasing the power density of the diesel piston engine. Among developments currently being investigated is the adiabatic diesel engine and the stratified charge rotary engine, both of which appear to offer possibilities for the future.

The adiabatic turbo-compound diesel engine has usually been discussed in the context of higher fuel efficiency, but it may also offer benefits in terms of volume and weight that will be of at least as much, if not greater importance, provided that they can be accompanied by acceptable levels of reliability. The most radical approach to date has been by one large US manufacturer, who has concentrated development efforts on the concept of a 'hot adiabatic' engine of 500bhp, in which the cooling system is completely eliminated; this is achieved by the use of ceramic materials to insulate the piston crowns, the face of the cylinder head, the tops of the cylinder liners and valve manifolds and ports. Difficulties have been encountered, however, in matching the thermal expansion and conductivity characteristics of the ceramic materials and the cast iron to which they are applied. Development continues, but it cannot be taken for granted that these problems will be solved; advocates of this type of engine nevertheless look further forward towards a minimum friction solution with gas-lubricated piston rings, unlubricated roller main bearings and solid lubricant coatings for other components.

Another unconventional approach to the problem of size and weight of future tank engines is a development of the rotary-piston Wankel, currently under investigation by another large US engine manufacturer. The advantages of the rotary piston principle include reduced volume and weight, mechanical simplicity and increased efficiency; it is likely also to prove cheaper per bhp than either conventional air-cooled diesels or gas turbines. Such advantages, coupled with an inherent multi-fuel capability and the combination of the diesel engine's economy with the gas turbine's

'smoothness', would make the rotary stratified charge engine a natural choice for the power plant of AFVs, if only the reliability could be improved. Wear of the rotor tip seals has so far proved to be the weak point of this type of engine; if this could be cured, the manufacturers predict an engine with an output of some 1,800bhp in a package weighing only 520kg. Reliability trials of a pre-production 2-rotor truck engine developing 75bhp are in hand at the time of writing, this and more powerful engines in the range having met their performance targets.

Other alternatives have been proposed, and some tested, for the powering of AFVs, including electric drive, tried during the First World War by the British and the French, during the Second World War by the Germans, the Americans and the British, and since then by the Belgians in their light Cobra APC; steam power engines using the Stirling cycle, and nuclear power. The foreseeable future, however, is likely to favour the gas turbine or the adiabatic diesel over any of these.

The purpose of the transmission in any vehicle is to apply engine power to the ground, and it must match the engine performance to the power needed by providing suitable speed relationships of engine and output to wheels or tracks. Unlike an electric traction motor, which can stop when the vehicle stops, the piston engine needs to be started up before the vehicle moves off and disconnected from the drive before the vehicle stops. From these requirements stem the following characteristics, which a transmission system must possess:

1. There must be a means of disconnecting the drive.
2. There must be a smooth system of engagement to connect the running engine to the stationary output.
3. It must be possible to vary the engine speed in relation to the output speed.
4. The engine's power must be transmitted from the engine to wherever the output is positioned.
5. It must be possible to drive the vehicle in reverse.
6. Facilities for reducing engine speed to output speed must be provided.
7. The installation must allow for any misalignments between engine and output.

While doing all this, the transmission must be light in weight, easy to operate, small in size and of a shape that is easy to instal in the vehicle, reliable and able to run for at least 4,000 miles between overhauls. It must also waste a minimum of power; any losses mean poor performance and waste of fuel, and must be dissipated as either heat or noise. For example, the output of the Centurion tank's Rolls-Royce Meteor engine was 650bhp at 2,500rpm; installation in the hot and crowded engine compartment and working with air cleaners and an exhaust system, only 550hp were delivered at the clutch. Losses in the transmission and the cooling fans accounted for a further 150hp, with the result that only 400hp of the engine's 650hp was available at the track driving sprockets to drive the tank. A typical figure for a tank gearbox is a need for some 80hp just to turn over the gearbox at maximum speed; but it is the power that is delivered to the sprocket or the wheels that matters in any AFV.

With the mechanical gear-change systems and pedal-operated clutches which were virtually standard in tanks up to the end of the Second World War, tank driving required great physical effort and skill on the part of the driver. In the Centurion, for example, the gear lever movements required great effort from the driver and the clutch pedal load was high; the limited engine power available at the sprockets meant that frequent gear changes were required, with the result that the driver was soon tired and failed to make the skilled gear changes of which he was normally capable. Later gearboxes, such as those in the British Chieftain and the US M-60, incorporated a 'hot shift' gear change which required little effort on the part of the driver and in which no time was lost during the change. In a fully automatic transmission, the driver does not even have to employ that skill which tells him when to change gear; the gearbox does it for him. Supplying a skilled driver with these facilities, however, does not waste them; it will leave him free to concentrate on other aspects of driving, such as selecting the best route across country, as well as tiring him less. The ideal transmission will provide an infinitely variable range of ratios, as in hydraulic or electric transmissions; these, however, have other disadvantages which have so far prevented their employment in military vehicles in service. With a stepless transmission, the engine can run at constant speed and maximum power; this ideal, however, seems unattainable in the foreseeable future, so that it will continue to be more normal to provide a stepped selection of gear ratios in the transmissions of armoured fighting vehicles.

Transmissions of tracked vehicles also usually provide for vehicle steering, by adjustment of the drive speed on one side of the vehicle relative to the other. In early tracked vehicles, steering was effected by means of clutches and brakes for each track; pulling the steering lever on the side in which one wished to turn caused the drive to the track on that side to be broken by the clutch and, by pulling the lever further back, the brake on that track to be applied. In this type of steering system, used in Soviet tanks, for example, until after the end of the Second World War, the power to the braked track was lost rather than being added to the other track; this clutch/brake system of steering was therefore known as a non-regenerative system and was very inefficient, being wasteful of engine power as well as requiring great physical effort in its use. Later transmissions incorporated regenerative steering systems, in which power lost in one track was applied to the other by means of some form of differential, thus requiring less effort in its use as well as being more efficient; such steering systems are known as controlled-differential (CLETRAC) systems in their simpler form and double or triple differential (Merritt) systems in their more refined versions. Ideally, a tracked vehicle's steering system should provide:

a. A minimum radius of turn linked to vehicle speed.
b. Transfer of power from the inboard to the outboard track (regeneration) during steering, with no power loss in the system itself.
c. Positive drive to both tracks at the same speed when not steering.

Modern tracked vehicle transmissions, such as those of the Challenger and Leclerc, incorporate infinitely variable, stepless hydrostatic steer systems in place of geared systems, as well as a hydro-kinetic torque converter to enable full power gear-changing and a lock-up clutch so that the transmission can be locked into gear drive. In the case of the Leopard 2, the transmission also incorporates an hydraulic retarder, as well as disc-type dynamic and parking brakes. Braking systems are generally also incorporated in the transmission, between the output and the final drive; in the Challenger, they are of the liquid-cooled multi-disc type, enclosed in the transmission casing. Final drives are usually of epicyclic type to give the final gear reduction to the sprocket drives, and are hull-mounted just inboard of the sprockets. As already mentioned, transmissions are now generally incorporated into a single unit known as the power pack, which includes the engine, fans and cooling system; the power pack is normally mounted on guide rails to enable it to be slid easily into or out of the engine compartment for maintenance or replacement purposes. Electrical, fuel and hydraulic connections are of the quick-connect type, self-sealing in the case of fuel and hydraulic pipes.

The engine and fuel systems of AFVs are potential sources of fire, particularly if the vehicle is penetrated in action. Statistics from the Second World War showed that 40 per cent of the total casualties sustained by tank crews came from burns. Engine compartments of most present-day tanks are therefore provided with fire detection, warning and extinguishing systems to enable such fires to be detected and extinguished before they can take hold. To be effective, such a system has to respond to the outbreak of an explosive fire in thousandths of a second; an effective suppressant is a range of halogenated hydrocarbons known as Halons, most of which are, unfortunately, toxic. Halon 1301 is, however, non-toxic in the concentration necessary to extinguish fires, and this is used in many AFVs today in conjunction with special infra-red detectors which can sense the radiation characteristics of a growing flame and generate a warning signal within two milliseconds. These detectors will not respond to other forms of electromagnetic radiation encountered on the battlefield; two suppressant stations in the crew compartment of a tank can extinguish a fuel fire in 60–100 milliseconds.

It is difficult to predict the form that the power pack of the AFV of the 21st century will take; that it will continue to comprise power plant, transmission, steering system and brakes seems incontrovertible, but it is the type of power plant and the type of transmission most likely to become predominant that is most difficult to forecast. The most attractive, on account both of its steplessness, its flexibility of installation and its relatively small volume would appear to be the electrical system. The petrol/electric form, in which a piston engine converts the fuel to rotational energy, which is then in turn converted to electrical energy, is a most inefficient method, particularly at the points where energy is changed from one form to another; but if such devices as fuel cells become a practical proposition, the energy in the fuel can be converted directly to electrical energy and electric traction could become an economic proposition. The development of solid-state rectification, inversion and frequency-change devices has increased the possibilities and made them more attractive.

Failing a breakthrough into electric drive and transmission, it is difficult to see any change from the present basic systems, employing either a compression ignition power plant of some sort or a gas turbine, in conjunction with mechanical step-change pre-selective or fully automatic gearboxes incorporating some form of retarder and hydrostatic steering system. It could be expected that the diesel engine would be one, such as the adiabatic, with considerably reduced cooling requirements, thus reducing the installation volume and increasing the power density of the engine compartment; alternatively, if the gas turbine were to be selected, it could be expected to follow commercial vehicle rather than aircraft standards and thus be cheaper and have a lower fuel consumption than those currently in service. Whichever power plant proves to be the best, there is no doubt that micro-processors will be used on an increasing scale both to optimize and harmonize engine and transmission performance and to maximize fuel economy. In any event, there can be no requirement for increased power output over those already available and in service; with lighter vehicles to power than the 60-tonne monsters of today, outputs of 1,000–1,500bhp would give power/weight ratios of 25–40bhp/tonne, more than adequate to give an excellent mobility and battlefield agility.

Since the First World War the majority of AFVs have employed a rear-engined layout, partly to give a better balance and more central centre of gravity in a turreted tank, and partly to give the driver adequate forward vision without unduly increasing the height of the hull roof. However, with turretless tanks carrying the ammunition in an auto-loader at the rear of the tank, which appears to be a likely future configuration, such an engine/transmission layout would make the vehicle rear-heavy, having an adverse effect on both its handling and its obstacle-crossing ability. If to this one adds that a front-mounted engine and transmission gives extra protection to the crew, it seems logical to expect this layout in MBTs introduced in the generation after Leclerc, Ariete and Challenger 2.

Most modern MBTs carry sufficient fuel to give them a road range in the region of 450 kilometres. Most stow this fuel internally under armour, until recently in sheet metal tanks adapted to the shape of the space in which they are to be fitted. It is Soviet and Warsaw Pact countries' practice to carry extra fuel in external tanks; this fuel is used for long approach marches, the tanks being jettisoned when empty and before the MBT goes into action. This was also British practice; during the Second World War, extra fuel was carried in jettison-able tanks at the rear of the hull or, in the case of the Churchill in Tunisia, in the hollow wheels of 2-wheeled Rota Trailers, with extra ammunition stowed in the trailer body. The practice was briefly continued in the 1950s, with the Centurion towing a mono-wheel trailer; it was discontinued, however, due to the restriction the trailer placed on the tank's manoeuvrability. The US Army also uses external fuel tanks, but the current British view is that, even if these tanks are jettisonable, the risks in air attack or ambush are too great; when it is necessary to keep the main fuel tanks full, 'jerricans' carried on the engine covers or the roof and discarded when empty are no more dangerous than external fuel tanks and much cheaper. In future AFVs, more use is likely to be made of flexible, self-sealing internal fuel tanks, which are better able to fill awkward internal shapes, can be inserted through much smaller open-ings in the hull, which are less prone to leakage through faulty welding or distortion and which present less of a fire risk if the tank is hit. Fuel can provide some protection against chemical energy projectiles, and this will be more fully discussed in the next Chapter.

We now come to the other main contributor to AFV mobility, namely the running gear; this comprises the road wheels, suspension and damping system and, in a tracked vehicle, the tracks. Of these, by far the most important is the suspension and damping system; there is irrefutable evidence that the main limitation on the cross-country speed of AFVs is not power but ride. The crew, even if harnessed, can tolerate only a limited amount of bumping, and there is a limit to the robustness that can be designed into optical, optronic and electronic devices; but both crew and devices must be capable of operating when their destination is reached. To increase this speed significantly, as is and will increasingly be required, improved suspension design is necessary.

The first tanks in the First World War were un-sprung; even at the very low speeds attained by these tanks, the crews experienced extremes of discomfort, largely due to the lack of any form of springing. As a result, most subsequent tanks were provided with springs of one sort or another, usually of metal although some employed rubber as the springing medium; in addition, they were fitted increasingly with rubber-tyred or resilient road wheels to absorb some

of the low-amplitude, high-frequency shocks imparted by the tracks. In some cases, rather than being sprung, road wheels were connected in pairs or larger numbers in a bogie pivoted to the tank hull; when the leading wheel of the bogie struck a bump, the bogie rose in the front about its pivot and the rear wheels accordingly dropped, thus smoothing the ride to a certain extent. In others, springs were combined with a bogie arrange-ment in order further to improve the ride.

The size of bump that can be dealt with by a spring depends upon how far upwards the wheel can move; this is usually limited by a resilient bump stop, so located that the wheel's vertical movement is stopped before the wheel can hit the hull. Unfortunately the bump cannot be ironed out, except by an aircraft or by an air-cushion vehicle not in physical contact with the ground, so that the wheel, and the vehicle, must follow the bump. The spring reduces the severity of a slight bump by moving the vehicle body so slowly that it is not disturbed much before the bump is passed and the wheel pushed down again by the spring. With a large bump, involving the wheel rising more than the available deflection, the wheel will rise quickly to the bump stop and hit it hard. On large bumps, a soft suspension that hits the bump stops will be more destructive of the vehicle than a hard one that does not; this problem will be aggravated if the suspension is not sufficiently damped, in which case vehicle bounce will add to wheel deflection.

In order to go fast over rough country, the suspen-sion must have the largest possible capacity to absorb the energy of impact on bumps. With soft suspension and inadequate available vertical wheel deflection, the vehicle will bump its suspension through to the stops. The initially soft ride will insulate the driver from any warning that he might have that he is working the suspension to its limits. By having a harder suspension, its resilience is greater, so that greater impacts can be taken without the suspension bumping through to the stops; the rougher ride gives the driver warning of the loads being put on the suspension, enabling him to adjust his speed accordingly.

From 1939 until the 1950s, the average available vertical wheel movement on AFVs was only some 8 inches; there were exceptions, notably the US Christie tank and its derivatives, the British cruiser tanks and the Soviet BT and T-34 of the Second World War, which provided very much greater deflections, and the British Churchill, with very much smaller ones. Sub-

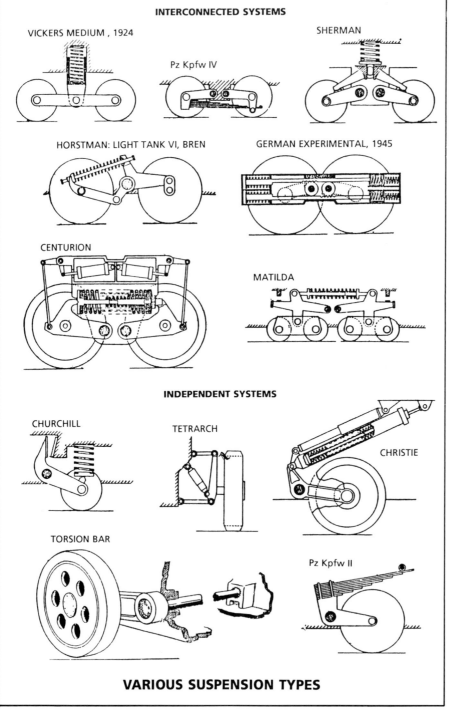

INTERCONNECTED SYSTEMS

VICKERS MEDIUM , 1924

Pz Kpfw IV

SHERMAN

HORSTMAN: LIGHT TANK VI, BREN

GERMAN EXPERIMENTAL, 1945

CENTURION

MATILDA

INDEPENDENT SYSTEMS

CHURCHILL

TETRARCH

CHRISTIE

TORSION BAR

Pz Kpfw II

VARIOUS SUSPENSION TYPES

▶ The British wartime cruiser tank Crusader had similar suspension and road wheels to those of the T-34. This is not surprising, since both were developments of the American designer Christie's pre-war design for a tank suspension allowing high cross-country speed. (Author's collection)

sequently, the trend has been towards greater vertical wheel movement, the British Challenger and the Brazilian Osorio having a total movement from the rebound to the bump position of some 18 inches and the Leopard 2 and M-1 Abrams, 20 inches.

By the outbreak of the war, the need for tanks to be sprung was universally recognized, and all those used by the combatants incorporated springing of one sort or another; because it provided the best compromise between performance, life, ease of maintenance and cost, the metal spring in one or other of its forms was the majority choice. In almost all British tanks, the helical (coil) spring was the chosen form, springing individual road wheels on the Churchill and the cruiser tanks, and in conjunction with bogie arrangements of two or more road wheels on all other types.

The Germans opted initially for semi-elliptic leaf springs on the Pz Kpfw I and II, early Pz Kpfw III and all Pz Kpfw IV; on later Pz Kpfw III, and on all Panther and Tiger tanks and derivatives, lateral torsion bars across the hull floor were preferred, while Dr. Ferdinand Porsche, ever the innovator, selected short longitudinal torsion bars in conjunction with 2-wheeled bogies for the Leopard, Elefant and Maus tanks which he designed. Due presumably to shortage of torsion bar manufacturing facilities later in the war, volute springs were substituted for the torsion bars in later versions of the Maus as well as in the Pz Kpfw III/

IV 'standard tank' being introduced at the end of the war. Of the 'E' series of tanks being developed at the end of the war, the E.10, 25, 50 and 75 employed Belleville washers, while the E.100 used helical springs.

The two main Soviet tanks of the war were the T-34 medium and the Klimenti Voroshilov (KV) heavy and its derivative, the Josef Stalin (IS); all three had independently sprung road wheels, the T-34 employing long helical springs mounted vertically inside the hull side plates and the KV and IS, lateral torsion bars across the hull floor. US tanks were, for the most part, fitted with volute springs, in either horizontal or vertical format, the wheels being sprung in bogie pairs; towards the end of the war, however, lateral torsion bars were beginning to find favour, being fitted, for example, to the M-24 Chaffee light tank which entered production in mid-1944 and the M-26 Pershing heavy tank, produced from November 1944.

Since the Second World War, the lateral, or transverse torsion bar has, until recently, been the almost universal springing medium for tracked AFVs; the only exception among the world's main tank-producing countries has been the United Kingdom, whose main battle tanks have used externally mounted springing systems, although torsion bars have been employed on their tracked reconnaissance and armoured personnel carrier families. There were several reasons for the British reluctance to use the torsion bar. In the first place, British industry lacked both the German know-how and the manufacturing capacity during the war to make highly stressed torsion bars suitable for AFVs; this was only gained after the war, when Allied teams descended on German infustry both to learn all they could about German manufacturing processes and to remove all the specialized machine tools developed for, and used in these processes. In the second place, British wartime experience with captured and knocked-out German tanks, and post-war experience with British prototypes equipped with British-made torsion bars had taught them not only that damaged torsion bars were extremely difficult to replace but also that the use of transverse torsion bars inside the armoured hull not only increased the tank height unnecessarily but that the extra hull volume thus requiring to be armoured added something like 1.5 tonnes to the tank's weight. These are general penalties paid by any internally mounted springing system; both the Soviet and British Armies discovered this with the width penalty imposed by the Christie vertical coil spring system used on the T-34 series and the cruiser series, respectively, during the war. The Soviets, however, substituted the torsion bar for the Christie system, thus trading a width penalty for a height penalty which, considering the importance attached by the Soviet Army to a low silhouette for MBTs, is surprising. A further disadvantage of transverse torsion bars is that, because they stretch from one side of the hull to the other, the bars on one side of the vehicle must be staggered behind those on the other; this gives a permanent 'bias' to the steering in one direction, thus putting an extra strain on the steering system and the driver. Finally, the vehicle width imposes a limit on the length of a simple torsion bar, and this in turn can limit vertical wheel travel.

The British Army did not make the mistake of employing a springing system that entailed a width, height or weight penalty; they opted instead for a suspension system mounted outside the tank, in the otherwise unused space between the top and bottom runs of the track. Not only did this obviate the height and weight penalties of the transverse torsion bar, but it also made very much easier the task of replacing broken or damaged units, while the extra metal outside the armour gave some measure of extra protection to the lower hull. The system used on the Centurion, the Conqueror and the Chieftain, as well as on the FV 4030/ 1 and 2 (Khalid), was a modified Horstmann bogie

system, in which the road wheels were mounted in bogie pairs sharing a common coil spring. While just adequate when the Centurion was first introduced, such a system allowed insufficient road wheel vertical movement for tanks with today's high power/weight ratios and this system was therefore abandoned in favour of a hydro-pneumatic suspension when the FV 4030/3, ordered by the Iranian Army but later taken over as Challenger by the British Army, was being designed. As will be seen, the new system shared with the Horstmann bogie the advantage of being mounted outside the hull, in space that was otherwise unused.

Despite the British aversion to the transverse torsion bar for MBTs, other countries have persisted with it, not only for MBTs but also for other tracked AFVs. The

◄
The running gear of the Soviet wartime medium tank T-34, showing the large diameter road wheels, on which the top run of the track is returned. (Author's collection)

British have also used them on lighter AFVs such as the CVR(T) family, the FV 432 family and the Warrior MICV, largely for simplicity; they are not, however, able to match the MBT for speed across country without the addition of complicated rotary dampers, a solution also adopted for the Leopard 2 and the M-1 Abrams and one which nullifies the simplicity of the torsion bar as a springing medium.

Whatever form it takes, a metal spring has the overwhelming disadvantage of having a fixed 'rate' or stiffness; that is to say that a graph plotting spring deflection against load will be virtually a straight line, when what is required is an increasing stiffness as the spring approaches full deflection. It is this disadvantage that is likely to signal the end of the metal spring

for cross-country tracked vehicles; even with the addition of a stiffer spring towards the end of wheel travel, the transition from one spring to the other is sudden and almost as much of a shock to the vehicle as hitting the bump stop. It is apparent, therefore, that some other springing medium is required, with characteristics more nearly matching the ideal of increasing stiffness with increasing load; such a spring is the gas spring which, combined with an hydraulic damper, gives us the hydro-pneumatic suspension system.

For many years, vehicle designers have sought to use a gas spring; gas under compression gives an almost ideal spring characteristic with the increasing 'rate' or stiffness under increasing load which is so necessary to the good cross-country speed of an AFV and the

77

comfort of its crew. Until recently, however, the sealing problems with such a spring and the heating problems with the integral damper, which exacerbated the sealing problems, had defeated them. The principle of the hydro-pneumatic suspension system involves the compression in a cylinder, by a piston connected to the wheel road arm, of an oil column, which in turn compresses a gas (usually nitrogen) as the spring medium; when the spring reasserts itself after being compressed, the fluid flows back through a damper pack in the cylinder, which damps the rebound of the piston and road wheel arm. This principle has been applied in single cylinder form to the Challenger, the Brazilian Osorio and the struts for upgrading the French AMX-13 light tank and the Centurion and Chieftain suspensions. Twin cylinder arrangements have been proposed by Cadillac Gage and Teledyne of the USA, SAMM and Messier of France and the West German firm of Frieseke & Hoepfner. Some of these employ an in-line arrangement and others an opposed arrangement of cylinders; while some are designed to be incorporated in the wheel road arm, others, notably those used on the abortive joint US/West German MBT 70 project and the new French MBT Leclerc, require a specially shaped hull side for their mounting.

Of course, the requirement for a special hull design removes one of the advantages of hydro-gas suspension and adds to the overall vehicle cost. On the US/FRG MBT 70, moreover, the units were mounted inside the hull, which had the twin effects of both narrowing the usable internal hull volume and causing the units to overheat due to lack of air circulation around them. Despite these disadvantages, however, the suspension of the MBT 70 performed well enough to convince many people of the feasibility of the hydro-gas principle for the suspension of tracked AFVs, with the result that it has been used on the Japanese Type 74 MBT for several years and is now in service on the British Challenger and shortly to enter service on the new French MBT Leclerc. The Swedish MBT StrV 103 (otherwise known as the 'S' Tank) was, however, the first production tank to enter service with hydro-gas suspension, in the late 1960s. This was a very original concept in many ways, dispensing as it did with the turret of more conventional tanks and laying the gun, which was mounted in the hull, by traversing on its tracks and elevating on its suspension.

The 'S' Tank illustrates one more of the advantages of hydro-gas AFV suspension, namely the ease with which it can be adapted so that vehicle height or

◄
The MBT-70 prototype with twin cylinder semi-active hydro-gas suspension at maximum height. The vehicle could also be canted to either side or tilted fore and aft by elevating selected units and depressing others. (Krauss Maffei)

◄
The MBT-70 prototype with its hydro-gas suspension at minimum height. (Krauss Maffei)

The 2-cylinder hydro-gas units installed in the MBT-70, showing how they were built into the hull structure with only limited air circulation available for cooling. (Frieseke u. Hoepfner)

A 2-cylinder hydro-gas suspension unit of the type installed in the US/FRG joint MBT-70 project. (Frieseke u. Hoepfner)

WHEEL TRAVEL: HYDRO–GAS STRUT COMPARED WITH TORSION BAR

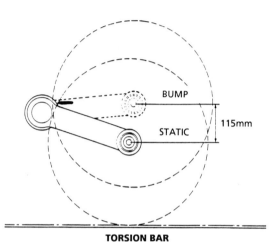

BUMP

STATIC

115mm

TORSION BAR

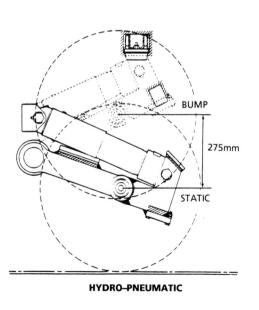

BUMP

275mm

STATIC

HYDRO–PNEUMATIC

attitude can be varied as required; this facility was provided on both the German and the US prototypes of the MBT 70, although with the penalty of considerable extra complication and cost. A suspension system providing the ability to alter vehicle height and attitude is known as a semi-active system; one without is known as a passive system. It will be possible in the future to adapt a hydro-gas system to be fully active, that is, a system that will automatically sense, and adjust to, bumps and other irregularities in the ground ahead before the vehicle reaches them, thus smoothing the vehicle's passage, easing the task of any sight or weapon stabilization system fitted and increasing the crew's comfort. Several prototypes of such systems have already been built and tested, in Britain, the USA and other countries, with varying results.

The most elegant solution to the hydro-pneumatic suspension problem is the single cylinder unit designed by the British for their Challenger and for the Brazilian Osorio. In this design, the oil and the gas are contained in the same cylinder, separated by a separator piston. When the road wheel meets a bump, the piston operated by the road arm crank forces the fluid rapidly through a damper pack, thus compressing the gas by means of the separator piston; as the wheel rebounds after passing the bump, the gas re-asserts itself, forcing the oil back through the specially sized orifices in the damper pack and thus damping the wheel's return to its normal static position. Experience has shown that not all units need to be damped; generally speaking, the front two units and that at the rear are damped, the remainder being undamped. With this design of unit, however, it is an easy job to insert or remove dampers, or to change the damper's characteristics as required.

With torsion bar suspension also it has been found necessary to provide external dampers, particularly on the rear and the front two units; experience has shown that friction dampers are not adequate for the job, and the preference of those using vehicles with torsion bar suspension is for hydraulic rotary dampers. These, of course, rather contradict the argument of proponents of this type of springing that it is simple and easy to maintain; this type of damper is no less complicated than, and is installed externally in the same place as, a hydro-gas unit, and at the same time one is paying the height and weight penalty imposed by the use of torsion bars.

The future as far as AFV suspension is concerned appears to lie with hydro-gas rather than with springs

TORSION BAR LAYOUT ON LEOPARD 2 (COURTESY KRAUSS MAFFEI)

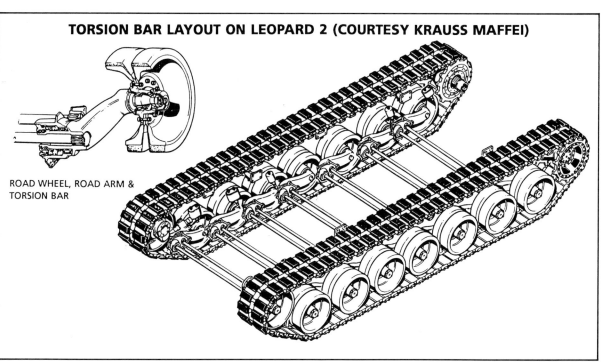

ROAD WHEEL, ROAD ARM &
TORSION BAR

HYDRO–GAS STRUT (SECTIONAL VIEW)

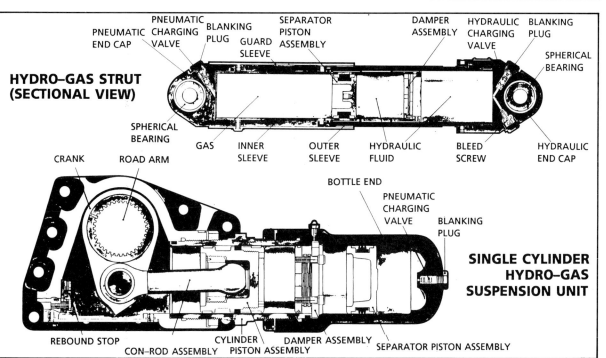

PNEUMATIC
END CAP

PNEUMATIC
CHARGING
VALVE

BLANKING
PLUG

GUARD
SLEEVE

SEPARATOR
PISTON
ASSEMBLY

DAMPER
ASSEMBLY

HYDRAULIC
CHARGING
VALVE

BLANKING
PLUG

SPHERICAL
BEARING

SPHERICAL
BEARING

GAS

INNER
SLEEVE

OUTER
SLEEVE

HYDRAULIC
FLUID

BLEED
SCREW

HYDRAULIC
END CAP

CRANK

ROAD ARM

BOTTLE END

PNEUMATIC
CHARGING
VALVE

BLANKING
PLUG

SINGLE CYLINDER HYDRO–GAS SUSPENSION UNIT

REBOUND STOP

CON–ROD ASSEMBLY

CYLINDER
PISTON ASSEMBLY

DAMPER ASSEMBLY

SEPARATOR PISTON ASSEMBLY

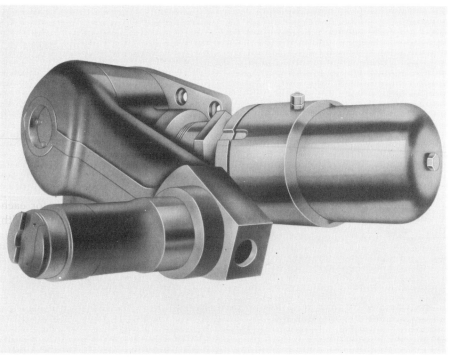

▲
Single-cylinder hydro-gas units installed on the Osorio MBT. Note that they are completely outside the hull and open to the air. This air circulation eliminates the overheating problems experienced with built-in units. (Engesa)

◄
A single-cylinder hydro-gas suspension unit, in this case for the Engesa Osorio MBT. Similar units are used on the British Challenger MBT. (Dunlop Aviation Division)

of metal or other material, and one can expect to see increasing unit life and lighter weight resulting from the discovery and use of new materials for seals and other components. Unit life between overhauls lies at present between 12,000 and 18,000 kilometres, which, considering how little annual mileage is completed by most tanks in peacetime, might be considered more than adequate; long periods of standing between use considerably reduce this life, however, by having an adverse effect on seals within the unit. The introduction of adaptive damping systems, in which the damping is adapted to the conditions is also possible; existing passive damping systems are always a compromise between high damping, to control resonance, and low damping, to reduce the transmission of high-frequency vibration and the generation of excessive heat in the dampers. One method of achieving such an adaptive system might be to use a damper in which the orifice size can be adjusted by an hydraulic servo-actuator, electronically controlled by means of wheel and hull velocity and acceleration sensors. One can also expect to see an increasing use of semi- and fully active suspension in future generations of tracked vehicles, particularly as new means of sensing the ground ahead, and of providing the power required to activate the suspension, evolve.

The remaining essential component of the mobility package is, of course, the wheel – and, in the case of a tracked vehicle, the track. For many centuries vehicles had run on wheels, but if the single most important step forward in mobility was the invention of the spark ignition and compression ignition engine, the most important contribution to allowing that mobility to be used by heavy vehicles across country in soft going was made by the invention of the endless chain track. First proposed in a British patent specification in February 1750, it was not until the early years of this century that any serious attempt was made to apply the idea commercially.

The main functions of an endless track may be summarized briefly as being to:

1. Provide multi-wheel drive from a single axle.
2. Increase the area of ground upon which a grip is obtained to drive the vehicle forward.
3. Distribute the pressure due to the weight of the vehicle over as large an area of ground as possible.
4. Improve obstacle-crossing performance by providing the equivalent of a ramp, and bridging the gap between wheels.

5. Provide an even, smooth roller path along which the road wheels can run with a minimum of resistance.

To fulfil these functions, each link of a track must have the following features:

6. A surface to rest on the ground, to give support.
7. A surface to engage the ground to give adhesion, either by friction or by digging in.
8. A wheelpath on which the load-bearing wheels can run.
9. Guiding faces to keep the wheels on the tracks.
10. Driving surfaces to take the drive from the sprocket.
11. A hinge for connecting it to the next link.

Various methods have been employed, since the first tanks were built during the First World War, to provide these features, not always with success. The tracks of the first British heavy tanks combined all the functions of a track very completely, but the increasing requirement for cross-country speed, and hence sprung suspension, rendered compromise necessary in later track design. The ground engaging surface will offer a certain amount of adhesion even if completely flat, and in some cases this adhesion has been considered sufficient for normal running; generally, however, it is not sufficient in many conditions, and it is not much improved by the provision of recesses in its surface, as these tend to become filled with earth. For optimum cross-country performance, the track link needs to present an aggressive face to the ground surface, and this is generally achieved by providing it with one or more raised transverse 'spuds' to bite into the ground. As such an aggressive face causes damage to roads in peacetime, modern track links are provided with replaceable rubber pads which bolt to the link and can be removed in wartime to expose the aggressive link face beneath.

The wheel paths on which the road wheels run are largely determined by the type of load-carrying wheels employed. Clearly, there must be a surface for each wheel to run on which is smooth and of adequate width to take the wheel tyre. The hinge joint must be so designed that the wheel will pass smoothly from one link to the next. Where flanged wheels are used, as, for example, on the Churchill of the Second World War, the edge of the wheel path can be relied upon for guiding, but with unflanged wheels the guiding face must be provided by upstanding projections (guide horns) on the track links. In the case of a single wheel there must be two guide horns, one on each side of the wheel path; with paired wheels, on the other hand, the opposite faces of a single guide horn will serve the purpose. There have been occasions, as with the German Panther and Tiger tanks, where two guide horns have been necessary, to serve triple or quadruple road wheels. Modern practice, however, is to employ twin wheel paths for twin, rubber-tyred road wheels, with a single central guide horn to guide both wheels.

The form taken by the surfaces for taking the sprocket drive to the track is again largely determined by the type of sprocket and whether single or twin sprocket drive is used. Normally, toothed sprockets are employed, the teeth of which engage in holes in the track links, but a roller sprocket was used on the US Christie fast tank and on the pre-war Soviet BT and the wartime T-34 tanks developed from it; in this case, the rollers engaged the track guide horns which served as the driving teeth. The almost universal modern practice is to use twin sprockets, engaging bosses cast into each track link. In many early types of track, as, for example, on the British First World War heavy tanks, the track links were in the form of plates stamped out of bullet-proof steel, riveted to a pair of chains which provided the hinge. In about 1927, forged links connected by a pin hinge started to replace the earlier built-up type, while, on the lighter tanks, cast links of skeleton rather than plate pattern began to be introduced. During the Second World War cast links of skeleton type, connected by a single dry pin, were introduced and standardized by the British, the Germans and the Russians; the Americans, however, preferred a double pin rubber-bushed and rubber-padded track on their tanks, a design which has stood the test of time and to which several other countries have now been converted.

Numerous different methods of connecting the links of a track have been tried, but the most common is the track pin which passes through lugs on adjacent links, rather as the pin in a door hinge. Dry, rubber-bushed and lubricated pins have all been used, the pins being held in place by split pins, circlips, anvil-and-sleeves, rivets, welding or even, in the case of the wartime Soviet T-34, by an inclined guide welded to the hull, which served to knock the track pins back into position as they moved past it. Pin wear is one of the commonest causes of track breakage, and this combined with wear of the track link lugs, through which the pin passes, causes the track to stretch; means of track adjustment must therefore be provided, and this is usually achieved by an adjustable idler wheel. The idler is mounted at the opposite end of the tank from the driving sprocket, and normally takes the form of the road wheels but with a smaller diameter; that is to say that, if twin, rubber-tyred road wheels are employed, with a central track guide horn, the idler wheels will also be twinned and carry rubber tyres. The adjustment of the idler to take up track slack is achieved by mounting it eccentrically; adjustment can be manual, by rotating a worm and wheel arrangement, or automatic. Too tight a track will limit suspension movement and increase both resistance to movement, thus wasting power, and stress in the track, leading to track breakage; too little track tension will lead to a slack track and consequent track throwing.

To improve adhesion under adverse conditions, numerous devices have been employed which can be attached to selected track links when required and removed when no longer needed. These can be used both to lower the ground pressure, by increasing the track's effective width, and to provide a more aggressive track profile, the better to bite into hard, slippery surfaces such as ice. These devices are generally known as 'grousers'.

Various track layouts, for supporting and carrying back the top run of track after it has passed under the road wheels, have been tried, as well as various numbers and diameters of road wheels. The early tanks employed a large number of small diameter, unsprung metal-tyred road wheels or rollers, some of which were flanged to retain the track, for the bottom run of track, the top run being returned round the top of the hull on phosphor-bronze guide rails or slides. The British wartime Churchill reverted to a similar system, only in this case all the road wheels were both flanged and sprung. The idea of having large numbers of small diameter road wheels was to even out the load on the track, spreading the vehicle's weight evenly throughout the track's bottom run; unfortunately, however, the smaller a wheel's diameter the greater its rolling resistance and the shorter its tyre life. With small wheels it is also difficult to provide large wheel movement and to keep the suspension out of the mud.

Experience world-wide has shown that the ideal suspension layout contains not fewer than five and not more than seven road wheels per side, of as large a diameter as is possible; with fewer than five, rolling resistance will rise sharply because the load points of the track are too widely spaced; it is better to have five

VARIOUS TRACK TYPES

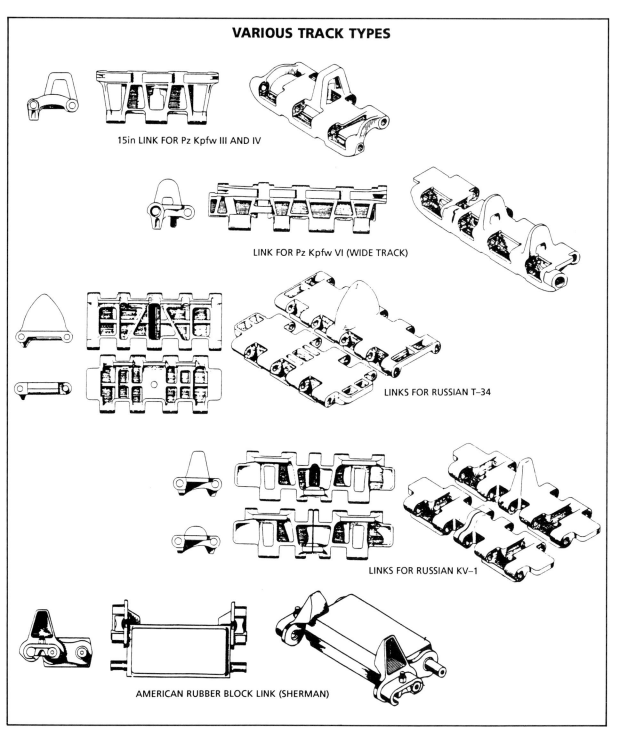

15in LINK FOR Pz Kpfw III AND IV

LINK FOR Pz Kpfw VI (WIDE TRACK)

LINKS FOR RUSSIAN T–34

LINKS FOR RUSSIAN KV–1

AMERICAN RUBBER BLOCK LINK (SHERMAN)

VARIOUS TYPES OF SPROCKET DRIVE

TRUNNION DRIVE

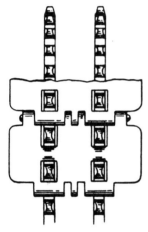

DRIVING BOSS
BETWEEN PINS

SINGLE SPROCKET DRIVE

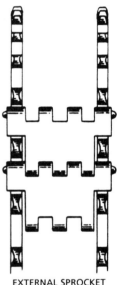

EXTERNAL SPROCKET
DRIVE

INTERNAL SPROCKET DRIVE

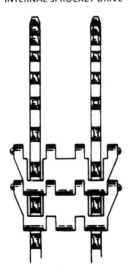

ROLLER SPROCKET

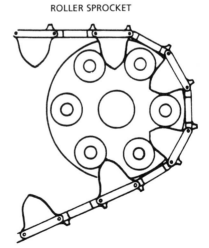

small wheels than four slightly larger ones, but the five should be the largest than can be squeezed in. With more than seven wheels, reduction in sinkage will be small and will be offset by increased weight. Most MBTs today have either six or seven twin rubber-tyred road wheels per side. On the basis that road wheels should be of the largest diameter possible, many tanks prior to, during and after the war had road wheels of big enough diameter to enable the top run of the track to be returned along their top surfaces; such tanks included the Soviet BT, T-34, T-44, T-54/55 and T-62, each with five road wheels; the British light tanks Tetrarch and Harry Hopkins and cruiser tanks A13 and Covenanter, all with four road wheels; the later British cruiser tanks Crusader, Cavalier, Centaur and Cromwell, each with five; the British Challenger with six; and the German Panther, Tiger and Royal Tiger, with eight or nine pairs of overlapping wheels. The German overlapping wheel layouts had the disadvantage of lack of accessibility when it was necessary to replace either a torsion bar or an inner road wheel; the overlapping wheels also had a tendency to pack with mud in soft going and added to the unsprung weight. These disadvantages more than outweighed the advantage of more even weight distribution.

Mention of increased unsprung weight will remind the reader that reduction of unsprung weight is one of the means by which tracked vehicle cross-country

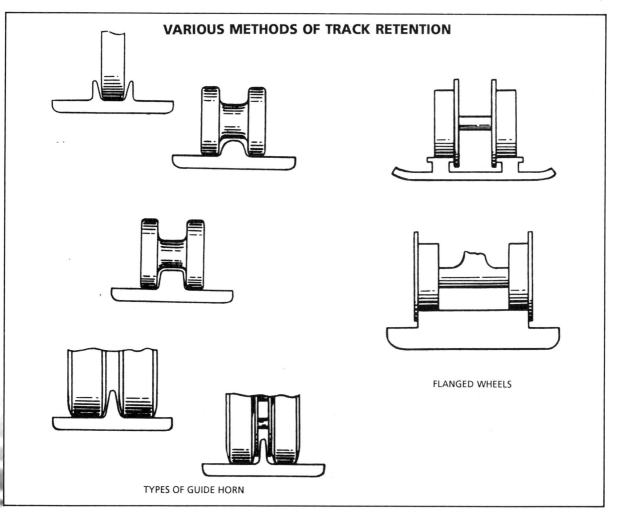

VARIOUS METHODS OF TRACK RETENTION

FLANGED WHEELS

TYPES OF GUIDE HORN

The running gear of the British wartime Churchill Infantry Tank, with multiple twin small-diameter flanged road wheels, independently sprung on coil springs. Small wheel diameter and vertical wheel movement did not permit of high cross-country speed. (Author's collection)

Typical twin screw propeller drive on an amphibious wheeled AFV, in this case the West German Spähpanzer 'Luchs' (Lynx). (Daimler Benz AG)

speed can be increased. Any increase in this weight is therefore to be avoided, if possible, and this was a drawback to the large-diameter road wheel carrying the returning top run of the track; the weight of the top run was almost entirely carried by the road wheels, and therefore added considerably to the unsprung weight. A preferable solution, subsequently adopted by all designers of modern MBTs and many designers of lighter tracked AFVs is to provide one or more small diameter wheels, known as return rollers, attached to the hull sides, to carry the top run of the track on its return run. Return rollers generally are twin rubber-tyred wheels running on the same wheel path as the road wheels.

From the solid, steel-tyred road wheels of the early tanks, flanged to guide the tracks, design has progressed through single rubber-tyred wheels pressed or cast in steel to today's twin rubber-tyred wheels forged in light alloy to reduce unsprung weight. The Germans and Russians experimented during and after the war with resilient wheels which had a steel rim retained in the wheel body by rubber bushes to give resilience; the aim was to increase the life of the road wheel tyre at a time of rubber shortage, but the life of such wheels was, if anything, shorter than the more conventional rubber tyre, as well as being very much noisier. Despite the many alternative tyre materials, both natural and man-made, which have been tried throughout the world in the search for increased tyre life, nothing to equal rubber has yet been found. The search will doubtless continue, in the hope of achieving not only longer life but also reduced unsprung weight.

True tactical mobility involves the ability to move not only across all types of terrain but also across water

obstacles, such as rivers, inland waterways and lakes, under the vehicle's own power. It may also involve crossing the strip of sea between a landing craft whose draught prevents it approaching closer to the shore and the shore itself. This means that apertures in the hull should be reduced to a minimum, and those that remain must be sealed against the ingress of water. The tanks of the First World War were not intended, neither would they have been able, to cross more than flooded shellholes or trenches without the aid of a bridge; their hulls were as full of holes as a sieve and would have been impossible to seal. After the war, however, the possibility of making tanks amphibious was investigated in Britain in 1919, when experiments with a Mark IX supply tank equipped with flotation chambers each side, a suitably raised cab and a modified exhaust system were carried out; the tank was

propelled by a small motor at the rear. In later experiments, a Medium D tank was propelled by its tracks, but steering in the water as well as exit from it proved difficult.

The trouble is that, for a vehicle to be truly amphibious, its design must be a compromise between those characteristics necessary to enable it to fulfil its role on land and those necessary to enable it to swim and manoeuvre in the water. Its buoyancy in water is governed by Archimedes' principle that flotation is given by a body displacing a sufficient volume of water to support its own weight; one cubic foot of water provides a buoyancy of 62.4 pounds. If a vehicle is not very 'dense', by having a squared-out body shape it should displace a sufficient volume of water for it to float without any extra aids; this is true of amphibious trucks such as the Second World War US DUKW, the post-war British Stalwart and US M-113 tracked APC, and the Soviet post-war wheeled APCs BTR-60 and BTR-70. Denser vehicles such as the post-Second World War British wheeled Ferret scout car and Saladin armoured car do not have sufficient displacement from their shape to float without the addition of a special rectangular flotation screen, while really dense AFVs such as main battle tanks need such vast screens to make them float as to make this method of water crossing largely impractical for them. Flotation as a method of water-crossing therefore has its limitations when applied to AFVs, particularly as the stability and manoeuvrability in the water of land vehicles modified to float is not very good. For many vehicles, the addition of a propeller, the most efficient propulsion system, or a water jet propulsion unit is not possible due to space limitations; in such cases, the vehicle has to rely on its tracks or wheels to propel it in the water, and special shrouding arrangements have to be made in the case of wheeled vehicles so that only the bottom of the wheels provides propulsive effort and for tracked vehicles, special arrangement of the steering gear so that one track is braked when the appropriate steering action is taken.

If the vehicle cannot be made to float it must wade through the water. Since before the Second World War, the fording depth of an AFV has been one of the more important design criteria specified when a new AFV is ordered. It has been customary for all tanks to be able to wade up to just below hull roof level without special preparation being required, the difficulty of sealing the turret ring and the level of the engine exhausts being the limiting factors; with special preparation, such as the addition of exhaust pipe extensions, disconnections of the cooling fans and waterproofing of engine ignition system, turret ring, gun mantlet and driver's hatches, it is possible to increase the wading depth nearly up to turret roof level.

In 1938 and 1939, trials were carried out in England of deep wading, in which long tubes were used to provide the submerged tanks and their crews with air, while the German Army used such a system in the crossing of the River Bug when they invaded Russia in 1941. The Germans refined this system when they designed the Tiger tank in 1941–2, building in to the turret ring an inflatable pneumatic sealing ring, as well as providing all hatches and all openings and vision devices with rubber seals, means of sealing off the normal air inlet to the engine and a stand-pipe or

snorkel tube through which air to engine and crew was admitted when travelling underwater. This pipe enabled the vehicle to operate when submerged to a depth of some 15 feet (5m). The post-war Federal German Bundeswehr has retained a similar system for its Leopard 1 and 2 MBTs, with which they have crossed both the Rhine and the Moselle, submerged, in trials and demonstrations, while the Russian and French Armies were so impressed by it that they have used it for all of their post-war MBTs. The German system enables their tanks to ford to a depth of some 12 feet (4m), the Soviet one to a depth of 14.5 feet (4.5m) in the case of T-54/55 and 17.8 feet (5.5m) in the case of the T-62, T-64 and T-72 MBTs. The Soviet tanks carry their snorkel tubes with them as part of their normal stowage, so that they can undertake a submerged river crossing at very short notice.

The British Army, having initiated the experiments with underwater obstacle crossing and having tried the method with both Centurion and Chieftain, have rejected this method of crossing water obstacles; if they are too deep for normal wading, the third method of crossing, by going over the obstacle on either a bridge or a ferry, being preferred. They rejected deep wading only after having tried towing, and remotely controlling uncrewed but suitably waterproofed vehicles across water obstacles; the waterway itself generally presents no problem, but egress on the far bank without assistance is always difficult. The British therefore favoured the employment of a pathfinder vehicle, equipped to winch itself out at the far bank and to winch out following vehicles; the Combat Engineer Tractor (CET) can be employed in this capacity, being equipped with a rocket-propelled earth anchor and suitable winches.

For crossing water obstacles, most armies have a certain number of bridgelaying tanks, based on the MBT chassis, carrying a bridge capable of supporting the current MBT and capable of bridging a gap of some 72 feet (22m) in the case of the British Chieftain AVLB, 60 feet (18m) in the case of the Soviet MTU-20 on the T-54/55 and 65 feet (20m) in the case of the German Leopard bridgelayer. For wider obstacles, use must be made of engineer bridging or ferry equipment. A fourth method of crossing water obstacles is by skimming the surface with an air-cushion vehicle; such vehicles have only limited application in ground forces, if only because of the difficulty of making sudden stops or changes of direction, but many of the problems encountered by other vehicles with egress from the water would be overcome by their use.

Armoured vehicles must be capable of moving by night as fast and as freely as by day, without the need to use an active lighting system using visible or infra-red light. In the past, invisibility of the light source was achieved by the use of headlamps filtered to emit only near infra-red light in conjunction with driver's and commander's periscopes able to convert near IR to visible light. The advent of passive viewing devices employing image intensification or thermal imaging, both of which can detect near IR emissions, or even the use by an enemy of near IR viewing devices in a passive mode, have rendered such methods obsolete. In the future, drivers will have passive viewing devices which need no extra illumination, in the form of either image intensifiers or thermal imagers; vehicle commanders are already being equipped with these.

Some form of navigation aid for at least AFV column commanders is especially useful at night and particularly so in desert or steppe country, or country so laid waste in nuclear or other attack as to lack recognizable landmarks. British forces in the Western Desert during and after the war made much use of the sun compass for daytime navigation in the desert, and the Germans were carrying out trials on a very sophisticated system on a Panther tank (Pz Beob Wg Panther) at the end of the war. Various systems operating on dead reckoning were tried by the British after the war, but it was found that errors due to track or wheelslip were too great to justify their introduction into service; in these systems, a gyro-compass was used to provide a heading, and both heading and distance travelled were combined to give a six-figure map grid reference to driver and commander. The introduction of navigation satellites, together with smaller, less sensitive but more accurate

◀
West German Leopard 1 MBT preparing to cross the River Mosel on the river bed. The commander is aloft, in his snorkel conning tower, which can be seen to assume alarming angles when negotiating river banks. (Bundeswehr)

An armoured vehicle-launched bridge (AVLB), in this case the West German Biber (Beaver), preparing to lay its bridge across an obstacle. (MaK)

gyros and electronic speed sensors opens up the prospect of cheap and accurate navigation by day or night in peacetime; how navigation satellites would fare in war is anybody's guess, but, as they could be of equal use to both sides, it is possible that they could be granted immunity from attack by common consent.

In this discussion of AFV mobility past, present and future, most of the emphasis has been on tracked vehicles; this has been because it is in the field of tracked AFVs that the future is likely to bring forth most change. We have seen that, in the quest for improved mobility, tracked AFVs of the future are likely to be lighter than their present counterparts, but with increased power/weight ratios and lower unsprung weight; hydro-pneumatic suspension with large wheel movement will be replacing the metal spring, giving dramatic improvement in ride and increased cross-country speed, with the possibility, if required, of semi-active systems for varying ride characteristics and vehicle attitude. Transmissions will incorporate infinitely variable ratios, hydrostatic steering and hydro-dynamic retarders, and microprocessor control of engine and transmission will give increased fuel economy. Passive night driving aids will become standard, and navigation aids will become cheaper and very much more accurate, based on the use of satellites.

Any discussion about the future of the AFV would, however, be incomplete without some indication of the advantages and disadvantages of the wheeled relative to the tracked vehicle, and ways in which the wheeled AFV might develop in the future. We have seen that wheels are preferable for AFVs of up to 5 tonnes in weight and tracks for vehicles weighing more than 20 tonnes or so. It is in the range from 5 to 20 tonnes, in which the majority of AFVs now lie, that the choice is an open one. For cross-country performance, neither system can be said to stand out from the other; it is only too easy to design a course that will show either to be decisively superior, so that, in this respect, choice is determined by the type of terrain in which the vehicle is most likely to operate. The advantages of tracks stem from the need to drive each track, and hence all the wheels on that side, from one point only; this drive also caters for steering and can be located at either end of the vehicle. In wheeled vehicles, every wheel must be driven, through a limited slip differential, and steered wheels must be driven through expensive and unreliable constant velocity joints; steer-

ing is normally Ackermann type, involving complicated and vulnerable steering linkages, and the lower hull has to be narrow to accommodate the wheels on full steering lock. Wheeled vehicles have the following advantages over tracked ones, even when Ackermann steering is employed:

1. There is no rigid L/C limitation on vehicle length as

there is with tracked vehicles.

2. They give a better ride.
3. They have better adhesion on hard surfaces.
4. A high sustained speed is easier to achieve.
5. They are quieter.
6. They give a greater fuel economy.
7. They do less damage to road surfaces.
8. Tyre life is much longer than track life.

To obviate the disadvantages of Ackermann steering, successful trials have been conducted, both in Britain and elsewhere, of multi-wheeled AFVs employing the skid-steer principle, as on tracked vehicles. If a wheeled vehicle employs a skid steer system, it has the following additional advantages:

9. The ratio of hull width to overall width is about the

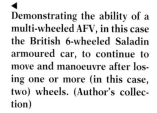

◄
Demonstrating the ability of a multi-wheeled AFV, in this case the British 6-wheeled Saladin armoured car, to continue to move and manoeuvre after losing one or more (in this case, two) wheels. (Author's collection)

same as for tracked vehicles.

10. Steering and differential action is contained in a single unit, as for tracked vehicles.
11. The system can accept a wrap-around track.

In view of the upper weight limit of 20 tonnes, therefore, there appears to be less scope in the future for radical change in wheeled than in tracked AFVs. For instance, there are many civilian commercial vehicle as well as military vehicle engines already in large-scale production with outputs able to give a 20-tonne vehicle almost any power/weight ratio that might be required; a similar position prevails with regard to transmissions. Improvements in these departments are likely, therefore, to be limited to microprocessor control to achieve maximum economy of fuel. Electric drive of individual wheels, with its infinitely variable speed range and ease of transferring the drive from the hull even to Ackermann steered wheels has attractions and possibilities, although some distance into the future. The most likely development, however, is the introduction of semi-active hydro-pneumatic suspension to give improved ride across country, with damping and spring characteristics variable by the driver to suit the 'going' conditions; for all its better ride when compared to tracked vehicles, the wheeled AFV does need greater vertical wheel movement to enable it to cope better with high-speed cross-country travel, and, as with tracked vehicles, the gas spring appears to offer the best prospect of achieving this.

Wheeled AFVs will require passive night-driving aids for both driver and commander, and the best prospect appears to be offered by thermal imaging; wheeled vehicles are more likely than tracked to be used for the armoured reconnaissance role, so that the greater cost of this type of night vision device over the image intensifier can be justified in view of the crucial importance of the best possible aids to accuracy of both navigation and observation in this role. Navigation aids will therefore be of the greatest value in this role, and one can envisage satellite navigation aids being issued down to troop/platoon commanders in reconnaissance units, as opposed to the probable scale of issue of one per squadron/company, or even one per battalion/regiment, in battalions or regiments equipped with main battle tanks.

Wheeled AFVs are fitted with tyres which can be run for a limited distance, say 50 kilometres, at a limited speed, say 50km/hr, after being punctured; various methods of achieving this are employed, some using inserts to prevent the tyre side wall collapsing and others relying on stiffened side walls for this purpose. None, however, is completely satisfactory in allowing the vehicle to travel as far and as fast as may be required; there is therefore scope for improvement in the design of 'run-flat' tyres in the future. The ideal tyre would be one in which the characteristics were unchanged after it had been hit, enabling the vehicle to continue its journey at maximum speed for as long as required. The development of such a tyre is, however, unlikely to occur in the foreseeable future, and will be dependent upon the discovery of some man-made material with characteristics superior to those of rubber.

It is a desirable characteristic of wheeled reconnaissance AFVs that they should be, to a certain degree, amphibious, and this is true of the Soviet BRDM, West German Luchs and, with some preparation, the British CVR(W) Fox. Ideally, they should also be equipped with some means of assisting egress on the far bank of any obstacle, and some means of propulsion and steering in the water other than their wheels. For egress, a winch and rocket-propelled earth anchor on the end of the winch rope probably provide the cheapest compromise solution, while for propulsion and steering in the water either built-in water jets with a steering facility or an outboard motor and propeller if water jets cannot be built in seem the best answer.

Wheeled armoured personnel carriers are little more than lightly armoured trucks, for the transport, mainly on roads and tracks, of troops behind the lines in forward areas of theatres of war. Their armour is sufficient only to keep out small-arms fire and shell fragments, and their design is likely in the future to follow multi-wheel drive commercial vehicle practice; their design presents no particular problems and does not, therefore, warrant further consideration here.

The preceding discussion has, it is hoped, covered the more important problems facing the AFV designer of the future so far as mobility aspects are concerned. It has also summarized briefly the main problems encountered to date and has offered some opinions as to the probable directions that future AFV mobility developments in the 21st century will take. It does not presume to be exhaustive, neither will it necessarily prove, in the light of hindsight, to have been accurate; it is, however, the best that can be done with the present standard of crystal ball.

PROTECTION

Ever since the kinetic-energy penetrating weapon was first invented, mankind has endeavoured to protect himself against it by carrying shields and wearing protective armour of one sort or another, to cover as many vulnerable parts of the body as was possible within the limits of his carrying and fighting capacity. Combinations of leather and metal sufficed to keep out at least some of the sword, knife and spear thrusts until the invention of the bow and its long rod penetrator, the arrow; this gave the attack a huge advance in both range and penetration, and a consequent advantage over the defence, until the invention of flexible metal armour did something to adjust the balance. The attack seized the advantage again with the invention of firearms, against which effective protection was too heavy for its wearing to be a practical proposition; for defence against them, reliance had instead to be placed upon concealment, surprise and movement under covering fire in the attack, and protective buildings or earthworks in the defence.

So, throughout the history of warfare, the balance of advantage has swung like a pendulum between weapons and protection against them. Even in 1487, Leonardo da Vinci, as engineer and painter, in the service of Duke Ludovico Sforza in Milan, was occupying himself with a design for a protected offensive vehicle, having told the Duke in his own testimonial when applying for the job: 'Also I can make armoured cars, safe and unassailable, which will enter the serried ranks of the enemy with their artillery, and there is no company of men-at-arms so great that they will not break it. And behind these, the infantry will be able to follow quite unharmed and without any opposition.'

The introduction of the rifle, the high-explosive fragmentation artillery shell and, finally, the machine-gun began a domination of the battlefield by fire that led to the stagnation of the trench warfare of 1914–18; both sides on the Western Front looked desperately for something with which to break the stranglehold which

▶
A model, made and exhibited by SCICON at the British Army Equipment Exhibition at Aldershot in 1982, of Leonardo da Vinci's 1483 proposal for an armoured fighting vehicle. Powered by four men, one per wheel, turning crank handles, the vehicle was very slow, almost impossible to steer, had a high ground pressure and the driving gears would have had only a very short life. (SD-SCICON)

the machine-gun exerted on the battlefield, some means of protecting advancing troops against the hail of machine-gun bullets which greeted anything that moved on the battlefield. In the event, it was the British who first came up with the idea of armouring a cross-country vehicle equipped with guns and machine-guns, with a view to restoring mobility to the battlefield.

Lacking Leonardo's self-, not to say over-confidence but possessing instead the priceless advantages of the internal combustion engine and the endless chain track, they were able to come up with a vehicle which, had it been properly employed in sufficient numbers, *en masse* instead of in penny packets over unsuitable ground, could probably have won the war in 1917. As

it was, lack of understanding of the tank's potentialities and best method of employment by the Allied, and the British High Command frittered away the advantage gained over the German Army by the shock of its introduction, with the result that it became just another weapon in the Allied war inventory and the war dragged on for another year.

The protection afforded to the crews of those tanks was minimal, but it was nevertheless sufficiently effective against ball ammunition fired from rifles or machine-guns, and against HE shell fragments from reasonably near misses, to enable the crews to move through MG curtain fire and artillery barrages, provided that the latter did not score a direct hit on the

▶
This view of the British First World War Mk V heavy tank brings out well the riveted armour construction. (Author's collection)

tank. Little was known in 1916 about the thickness of steel that could be penetrated by small-arms ball ammunition or HE shell fragments, so that, when the idea of an armoured fighting vehicle was first mooted in Britain, arbitrary decisions as to material, thickness and hardness had to be made. Electrical welding was not available at that time, neither had the high-speed drill then come into use; armour steel was made, cut and drilled as mild steel, subsequently hardened to resist hostile fire, and the tank was built out of it by riveting sheets of armour plate to butt straps and angle iron. This was the method used in the building of water tanks, and it was the use of this process that gave the idea for the cover name 'tank', used to conceal from the

public and enemy spies what was actually being built. The name stuck, and tracked armoured fighting vehicles have been known, at least in the English language, as tanks ever since that time. The gaps which inevitably resulted from this method of construction allowed molten lead, known as 'splash', from disrupted bullets to penetrate the inside of the tank whenever the joints were hit by small-arms fire.

Considerable trouble was experienced with the armour plate; hardening presented many problems and plates were liable either to crack during the process or to be so brittle that they failed due to the strains and stresses imposed upon them by the tank's motion. The amount of armour was limited by the need to limit the overall weight of the tank, partly for reasons of soft ground pressure and partly due to the limited engine power available. The Marks I, II and III had a thickness of 10mm on the front and 8mm on the sides; these were the thicknesses, obtained from captured tanks, on which the German designers of armour-piercing ammunition worked when designing ammunition to defeat the tanks. When the Mark IV was introduced, therefore, with 12mm plate on both front and sides, it possessed a very real and substantial advantage over the German anti-tank defence.

Bullet splash considerably hindered observation by the crew; to minimize its effects tank crews were issued with extra protection in the form of steel face masks, with a chain mail visor hanging from the lower edge. The introduction of this device reduced casualties, but it also hampered observation.

The experience of firms concerned with the manufacture of naval armour was sought initially, but battle experience with tanks soon showed that armour on land would have to withstand types of attack different from those to which naval vessels were subjected, and it became necessary both to modify the materials used and to include others hitherto unused in naval architecture. Production methods too were different; whereas warships required small numbers of very large plates, tanks were built from many small plates and castings. Nevertheless, the Armoured Car Division of the Royal Naval Air Service was given the responsibility for the development of light armour for the British tanks; rolled nickel steel plate was used.

One form of attack to the defeat of which special attention was devoted in 1916 by British tank designers was the direct hit by high-explosive artillery shell; experiments were carried out which showed that a ³⁄₈in plate placed 12 inches in front of the main plate was sufficient to detonate the shell and prevent any damage to the tank. As will later be seen, this lesson was soon forgotten and the uses of spaced armour needed to be relearned by both sides during the Second World War; it was the difficulty of mounting these spaced plates, as well as the extra weight entailed in their use, which prevented their introduction. It was not until 1934, with the introduction of the first 'Infantry' tank, that the British General Staff specified armour thicknesses in excess of 14mm. 25mm of armour was specified for the Infantry Tank Mark I, with the idea of defeating the British 15mm BESA machine-gun and Boys anti-tank rifle, such a thickness not being adequate for defeating the continental 37mm guns then being mounted on their tanks or used as field anti-tank weapons; this British habit of specifying protection standards against their own weapons was persisted in right up to 1940, and was the cause of much of the under-armouring that so reduced the fighting efficiency of British tanks during the Second World War. The cause was presumably inadequate technical Intelligence concerning foreign weapons and equipment. Riveting and bolting continued to be the main armour assembly method used for tanks up to the Second World War, and rolled homogeneous steel armour plate the main armour material.

The tanks with which the British entered the Second World War were built by riveting armour plates on to an angle iron framework. The plates had to be cut by guillotine, after which their edges had to be ground to give a close fit and make them proof against bullet splash; large numbers of holes had to be drilled to take the rivets, or drilled and tapped to take bolts, and these operations caused very high consumption of expensive drills and taps, as well as increased labour costs. Furthermore, under impact from projectiles, bolts and rivets would become dislodged, flying about inside the tank and causing as much damage as the projectiles themselves. The making of all joints watertight for the fording of water obstacles and the crossing of marshy ground was also difficult to achieve with this method of construction.

Alternative ways of fabricating armoured hulls and turrets were therefore investigated as the need for more rapid production made itself felt. The obvious answer from a production standpoint was to gas-cut all plates to the correct profile by machine, and to fabricate the hull and turret using arc welding, pro-

vided that no reduction in immunity or serviceability resulted. Far from a reduction in immunity resulting, ample evidence was produced to show that the welded tank would be superior under attack in battle, while at the same time its inherent structural rigidity was an important means of reducing stresses and consequent wear in running gear and turret traverse rings and mechanisms. By the use of well-designed jigs and manipulators, in which the hull or turret could be rotated to ensure 'downhand' welding of the joints, fabrication could be greatly speeded up compared to the earlier method using rivets. In Britain, however, there was a marked reluctance on the part of British Industry to adopt the welding provess for the fabrication of tanks, despite the fact that the Government-owned Woolwich Ordnance Factory had carried out the necessary research and development and a fully proved technique had been available to them since before the Second World War. Many British tank crewmen's lives would undoubtedly have been saved if apathy on the part of Industry had not prevailed over Government inducement. Not all the blame lies at Industry's door, however; the War Office itself was not convinced until much later of the benefits of the welded tank. Germany, by contrast, had started to use all-welded construction for her tanks even before the outbreak of war.

Further assembly time was saved by the use of armour castings; initially, as in the case of the British Infantry Tank Mark II Matilda, for sub-assemblies but later for complete turrets and, in the USA, hulls. The French had made considerable progress in the use of hull and turret castings since first introducing them on the R35 and H35 medium tanks in 1935 and up to the time of her defeat in 1940 by the Germans. The Soviet Union made extensive use of armour castings on the tanks introduced during the Second World War, the T-34, KV and IS, and has continued to do so on all its post-war tanks. The USA, Britain, West Germany and France have also made considerable post-war use of armour castings in their tanks, not only for turrets but also for parts of the hull. The use of castings enables curved shapes to be employed, thus enclosing the required volume more efficiently as well as presenting a more difficult target to the incoming projectile.

Prior to the introduction of cast armour, the front of a tank hull, constructed from a series of riveted or welded flat plates, tended to follow the outline of the seated driver and co-driver it was protecting, with a

The British Matilda Infantry
Tank of the Second World War
made early use of cast armour
for its turret and front nose
plate. (Author's collection)

This close-up of the front of a
US M-3 tank knocked out in
Tunisia in 1943 shows clearly
the riveting of thicker armour
plate. (Author's collection)

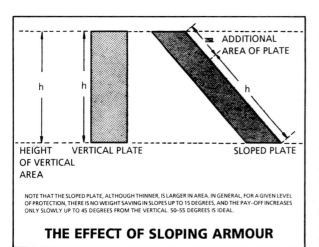

HEIGHT
OF VERTICAL
AREA

VERTICAL PLATE

SLOPED PLATE

NOTE THAT THE SLOPED PLATE, ALTHOUGH THINNER, IS LARGER IN AREA. IN GENERAL, FOR A GIVEN LEVEL OF PROTECTION, THERE IS NO WEIGHT SAVING IN SLOPES UP TO 15 DEGREES, AND THE PAY–OFF INCREASES ONLY SLOWLY UP TO 45 DEGREES FROM THE VERTICAL. 50–55 DEGREES IS IDEAL.

THE EFFECT OF SLOPING ARMOUR

near vertical plate (known as the front vertical plate for that reason) protecting the upper parts of their bodies, a nearly horizontal plate (known as the glacis plate), extending from their waist to their feet, protecting their legs, and another nearly vertical plate (known as the lower nose plate) protecting their feet. Most of the remaining hull plates were vertical or nearly so, with the exception of the belly plate and the hull roof, which were horizontal, and any sloping of plates was purely for weight-saving reasons, rather than to make a more difficult target.

Similarly with turrets; sides tapered only slightly from turret ring to roof, more to accommodate the taper of the crewmen's bodies from shoulder to head then for any reason of terminal ballistics. There was usually a 'bustle' at the rear of the turret, which projected beyond the turret ring over the hull roof and was used to house radios or ammunition; the space between the turret bustle floor and the hull roof was later recognized as being a shot trap, tending to deflect striking projectiles downwards into the hull. Similar tendencies were noted during the Second World War with certain designs of gun mantlets, and designers tried to avoid these in later tanks. Vision slits, backed by thick bullet-proof glass, were provided for drivers, as well as periscopes projecting through the hull roof or mounted in the driver's and co-driver's hatches. Vision slits, protected by glass blocks, and pistol ports were also originally provided in turret sides, but towards the end of the war it came to be realized that such openings were little used and represented weak points in the armour protection.

Experience during the war, however, completely changed the views of all the major combatants on the armour protection of AFVs, particularly when the Soviets introduced their T-34 medium tank in November 1941; up to that time, the increasing superiority of the anti-tank gun had been countered by the addition of extra, appliqué armour plates at vulnerable points, the basic shape and outline of the tank remaining unchanged. There was, however, a limit to the weight of extra armour that could be applied in this way, and added armour is, in any case, not as effective as homogeneous armour of a lesser thickness than the combined thickness of basic and appliqué plates. The basic change came with the realization that sloped armour presented a very much more difficult target to the anti-tank projectile than vertical armour, and that valuable weight could thus be saved without sacrificing protection; most anti-tank projectiles hit a target with an almost horizontal trajectory, and it can readily be seen that a vertical plate will present the minimum thickness to horizontally-striking projectiles. By sloping the plate, the ideal slope being in the region of 55° to the horizontal, its effective thickness is greatly increased, and the penetrative task of the projectile made more difficult in consequence. The Soviet T-34 embodied this principle in a hull shape that has formed the basis, with minor variations, of the majority of subsequent MBTs worldwide, starting with the German Panther and Royal Tiger and carrying on through Centurion, AMX-30, and Leopard 1 to the present day.

Distribution of the available weight of armour in any AFV design has always been a vexed question, to which there is no universally correct answer. Given a specified number of tons of armour with which to protect an AFV without overloading, what proportion should be allotted to the front? The sides? The roof? The belly? The turret? Is there any point in having frontal armour thicker than the sides? Should the turret be better protected than the hull? These are some of the questions which present themselves with any new design of AFV, and which have to be answered in relation both to the vehicle's prospective role and to the theatres of war in which it might be involved. Two points which are fairly clear are that, first, almost any given user will ask for more armour in the place where his tank was most recently hit, and, secondly, that it is almost impossible, and most certainly unwise, to design for any particular condition; a balance must be

TYPICAL ARMOUR ARRANGEMENT AND DISTRIBUTION (SOVIET T-34)

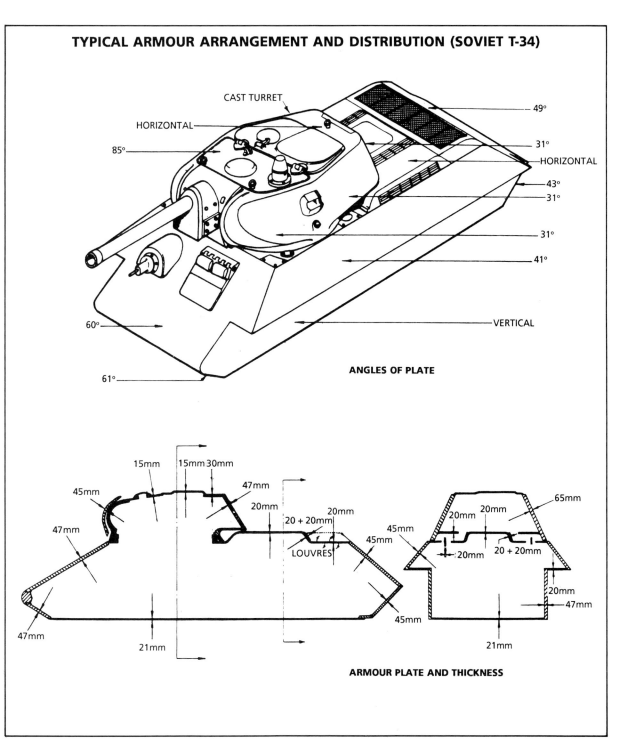

ANGLES OF PLATE

ARMOUR PLATE AND THICKNESS

Cut-away line-drawing of the Soviet T-34 medium tank.

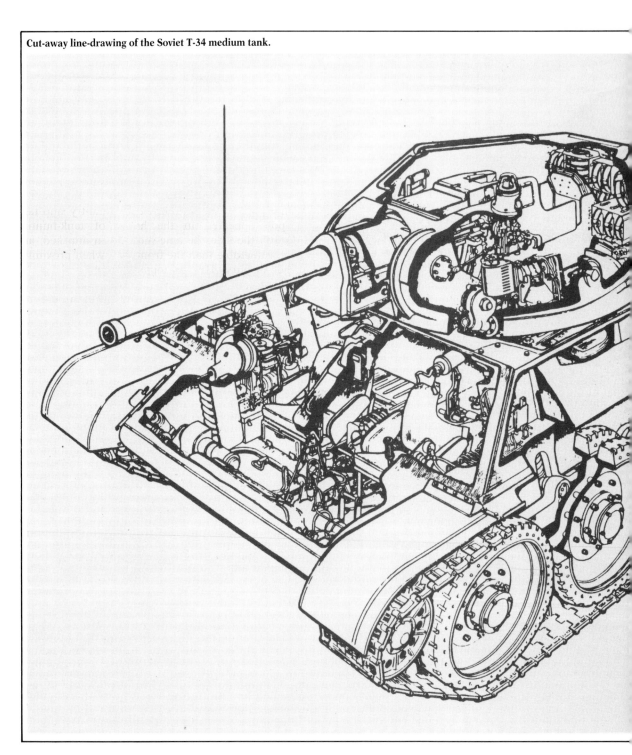

struck between all the conditions that might be encountered.

In Britain between the wars, the development of an armour distribution theory was comparatively neglected; although many of the problems were known and appreciated, they were not precisely formulated. The lack of an adequate theoretical approach led to a failure to appreciate the importance of making the frontal armour immune to attack and not merely thicker than that of the sides. The general vulnerability of an AFV increases very rapidly as soon as the front ceases to be immune. But conditions change, and as soon as the German *Panzerfaust* infantry anti-tank weapon appeared in the hands of tank-hunting infantry, the sides became more often attacked, and more vulnerable than the front; and when proximity-fuzed air-burst HE, or top-attack anti-tank guided weapons appeared, the roof became in turn the more vulnerable. There is, therefore, no set answer to the problem of armour distribution; the presence on the modern battlefield of top-attack weapons with heat-homing warheads, however, together with the threat from attack helicopters means that very much more attention will have to be paid to the top armouring of future AFVs if they are to retain their advantage of protection.

Prior to, and during the first half of the Second World War, attack of armour was carried out mainly by high-velocity guns whose projectiles penetrated armour by means of their kinetic energy; these projectiles were almost universally solid steel shot, ballistically shaped to minimize velocity loss in flight. The other type of attack was the anti-tank mine, which was detonated by the passage of a tank and achieved its effect by disrupting the tank's belly, breaking its tracks and blowing off its suspension units. Most armour was of homogeneous steel, although the Germans employed face-hardening on certain plates which caused British solid shot to shatter at certain angles of attack; to counter this, the British fitted a penetrating cap to their shot, which, on striking the target at an angle, formed a basis around which the shot could pivot so that it could attack the plate at 90° (known as 'normal' attack). As a counter to this ploy, the Germans fitted spaced armour, supported on brackets some 12in to 18in from the main armour, with the aim of stripping the caps off projectiles before they could strike the main armour. As muzzle and striking velocities and weights of KE projectiles increased as the war pro-

The wartime German Pz Kpfw IV, Model H shown here is a good example of the use of spaced armour on both turret and hull sides. Its purpose was to strip the cap and ballistic cap off APC and APCBC projectiles, thus reducing the ability of the projectile to penetrate the main armour. (Author's collection)

gressed, so the thickness of armour required to defeat them increased and the need for sloping the armour to increase the effective thickness became urgent.

With the German introduction of the *Panzerfaust* and other infantry anti-tank weapons firing chemical energy HEAT projectiles, and of hollow-charge shells for conventional guns, a new dimension was introduced into the attack of armour. It soon became apparent that the HEAT projectile could defeat the thickest armour that it was practicable to put on a tank, provided that a hit could be obtained; this was admittedly more difficult than with a KE projectile, as fuzing and the distance from the plate at which the shell was detonated were critical to correct functioning, and the muzzle velocity, and hence the accuracy, was much lower than the flat trajectory KE projectile. Against HEAT attack, spaced armour was useless; the jet initiated by the strike on the spaced plate easily penetrated it, crossed the air gap to the main plate and went on to penetrate that also. Due to the very great penetrative power of the HEAT jet, increasing the effective armour thickness by sloping it made little if any difference, and it rapidly became apparent that, unless some radical new method of protecting against HEAT attack were developed, the thickest armour it was possible to use on the battlefield of the future could

be defeated with ease by any lone infantryman with nothing more expensive than a shoulder-launched projectile at short ranges or an anti-tank guided missile at longer ranges. After the war, another form of chemical energy attack was developed by the British to make the AFV designer's life still more difficult; this was the squash-head projectile known in British service as HESH (HE Squash Head) and in the American as HEP (HE Plastic). It was soon discovered, however, that an air gap nullified the disruptive effect of this type of projectile, so that spaced armour was effective in countering it. It is nevertheless useful to keep it in the attack of armour inventory, mainly because it keeps the opposing armour designer guessing and forces him to take its possible use into account, but also because it has a passable secondary function as a high-explosive projectile.

It was, however, the threat posed by the HEAT round that was the most urgent problem for AFV designers after the war; with the more sophisticated fuzing and projectile design that began to appear, the balance between anti-armour weapons and protection against them had swung steadily in favour of the attack, to the extent that many people were once again predicting the demise of the tank. Something had to be found to redress the balance, and the search for a method of doing so was given very high priority in defence research and development establishments throughout the world.

One of the most promising approaches to reducing the vulnerability of armoured vehicles is undoubtedly to reduce drastically the frontal area, particularly that area which must be exposed in a direct fire engagement; much design investigation into methods of achieving this continues to take place, notably into methods of dispensing with the conventional turret. Other approaches have concerned themselves with replacing the smooth, sloping homogeneous steel armour with something that will give better protection specifically against HEAT attack; one of the first alternative materials to be tried, first in the USA and later elsewhere, was aluminium.

US experiments with aluminium armour in the mid-fifties arose largely out of the surplus aluminium production capacity made available in the USA by the sharp fall-off in the demand for aluminium for military aircraft, brought about by the end of the Korean war; this made the aluminium producers look for alternative applications for their products. This happened more or less simultaneously with the placing by the US Army of increased emphasis on the air transportability of its equipment. The benefits of replacing steel with aluminium were, however, by no means clear cut. The lower density of aluminium meant that, for a given degree of protection against artillery shell fragments, a weight saving of more than 15 per cent could be achieved by its use; against attack by hard-core, ballistically shaped projectiles such as AP small-arms ammunition, however, it was found that, to obtain the same degree of protection as steel, aluminium armour had to be about three times as thick as its steel counterpart and the weight of the two was virtually the same. One of the benefits of using the thicker aluminium, however, was the greater structural rigidity of hulls and turrets made from it; in consequence, a number of purely structural stiffeners could be eliminated in the construction of aluminium hulls, thus saving both weight and production man-hours. Machining and welding speeds are faster with aluminium than with steel, once the technique of welding has been mastered, and it is possible, due to the greater plate thickness necessary with aluminium, to use stepped rather than mitred weld joints, requiring less welding and giving greater strength. The alloys used are of aluminium/zinc/magnesium, heat-treated to

improve their ballistic characteristics; however, they are suitable only for light armoured vehicles up to 20 tonnes in weight, as, even if aluminium armour proved effective against large-calibre high-velocity tank guns, the great thicknesses required make it unacceptable for space reasons on main battle tanks, unless used in combination with other materials. Stress corrosion cracking of welded joints is a danger with aluminium armour, unless particular care is taken in the welding; it has also called for the avoidance of machining or drilling of holes in the neighbourhood of welded joints. Aluminium armour has been used with success in the US M-113 and 114 APCs, the M-2 and M-3 Bradley fighting vehicles and the M-551 Sheridan light tank as well as in the British CVR(T) and (W) series of light reconnaissance vehicles.

In the search for a way of defeating the all-conquering HEAT projectile, the sloping of armour to defeat the high-velocity KE projectile was found, if anything, to aid penetration of armour by the HEAT jet; the lower striking velocity and steeper trajectory of gun-fired HEAT projectiles meant that they were more likely to strike the armour at an angle nearer to 90°, while the extra distance that the jet had to travel to penetrate a sloped plate presented it with no problem. Incidentally, while talking about sloped armour it should be mentioned that the British and US authorities describe a slope as an angle to the vertical, while continental practice is to describe it as an angle from the horizontal; this is most confusing and, if misunderstood, shows British and US AFVs to apparent disadvantage.

Methods of defeating the HEAT projectile by deflecting it, or disrupting the conical liner of the HEAT explosive charge at the moment of strike were also investigated. Attempts to cover the armour with a multitude of long spikes, in the hope that the projectile would strike one before hitting the armour and thus disrupt its cone, were unsuccessful as well as being most inconvenient to the crew and vulnerable to damage from trees. Ribbed, bar and grill armour, developments of the spaced armour concept, were also tried; in bar armour, deep metal ribs were fitted perpendicular to the outside of the armour plate, while in the other types, rods or slats were held in a frame, supported at a specified distance from the armour. The result in all three types against HEAT attack was found to be unpredictable; the ribs might damage the fuze or the explosive charge should the shoulder of the shell or warhead impact on them, or they might turn the shell

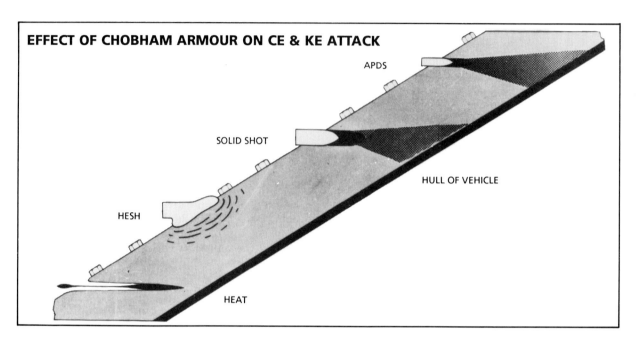

EFFECT OF CHOBHAM ARMOUR ON CE & KE ATTACK

APDS

SOLID SHOT

HULL OF VEHICLE

HESH

HEAT

so that the jet discharged harmlessly across the armour. On the other hand, they might set the projectile up for an ideal attack.

Some other means of defeating HEAT attack had to be sought, and thoughts were accordingly turned to compound armour, in which an arrangement of layers of various materials, backed by steel, would replace the conventional homogeneous steel. Many combinations were tried with varying success in various countries; quite early in the research, glass was discovered to have a jet-resisting capacity very much greater than might have been expected, being more efficient than mild steel even on a thickness-for-thickness basis. As a result, despite its obvious weakness against KE attack, the Americans have done much development work on siliceous-cored armour, in which blocks of fused silica are used as cores in cast armour and the resulting panels appliquéd to the main armour.

Other heat-resistant materials such as carbon and asbestos have also been tried, but it was not until the British military vehicle research and development establishment at Chertsey, near Chobham in Surrey, finally came up with the combination now known as 'Chobham Armour' in the early 1970s that an answer to the HEAT projectile really seemed to have emerged. The US Army announced in 1988 the introduction on the M1A1 Abrams MBT of a composite armour incor-

CROSS–SECTION OF US M1A1 ABRAMS MBT

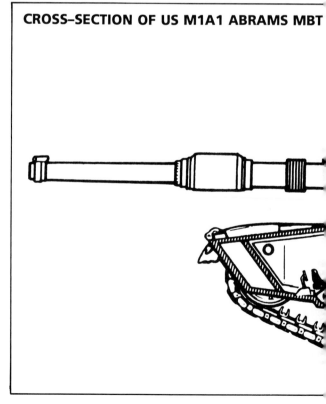

porating depleted uranium encased in steel; depleted uranium has a density some 2.5 times that of steel and is a by-product of the nuclear power industry. Its use on the previously Chobham-armoured M1A1 will increase the weight of the tank by some 1.8 tonnes and will be added to the vehicle on assembly rather than retro-fitted.

Although intelligent guesses as to the materials involved in Chobham armour can be made, no official information about its construction has ever been publicly released, although the secret has certainly been shared with both the US and West German authorities in the course of abortive joint tank development programmes. Once an enemy knows the details of a protective system, he can counter it more easily than we can modify it, so that information on protection against specialized anti-armour weapons must be guarded with particular care, being released only to those whose 'need to know' is beyond doubt.

Compound armours offer very great possibilities for the future, and have, in fact, been adopted for the British Challenger and most Western tanks of this generation. They tend to be bulky and difficult to manufacture in compound shapes, which accounts for the great external similarity between the slab-sided MBTs of the current and next generations; they alter the whole structural design concept of a vehicle. For full effect, they must be designed to counter a specific form of attack and on this basis can deal with any foreseeable power of attack; compromise systems to protect against both KE and HEAT attack are feasible, but, for a given weight and bulk, their effectiveness against either mode of attack will be considerably, and perhaps critically less than that of a single-purpose system. Developments in compound armour have at last swung the balance back from the anti-armour weapon to the tank; in a vehicle of MBT class, complete frontal protection against any single mode of attack can be achieved by the use of this type of armour. It does, hoeever, add to the already excessive weight of the modern MBT; conventional steel armour can normally be reckoned to account for some 50 per cent

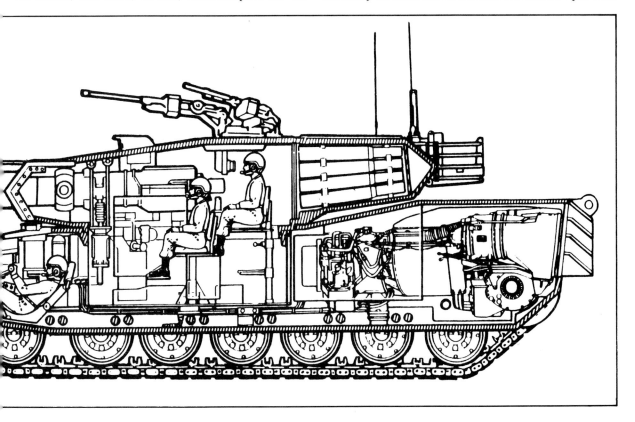

of the weight of the average turreted MBT, but the addition of compound armour increases both the weight of armour and the percentage of total vehicle weight which it occupies. In view of the development of weapons which home on the heat generated by an AFV and attack it from the top, extension of the principle of HEAT-defeating compound armour to the roof surfaces of future MBTs may well have to follow.

A well-designed armoured vehicle will have inherent all-round immunity to a very high proportion of the non-specialized weapons it may encounter on the battlefield from the metal necessary to give it structural strength; these will include medium artillery shell fragments, 12.7mm MG ball ammunition and direct hits from conventional HE shell of up to 105mm calibre. Any attempt to go beyond this amount of protection, however, will incur severe penalties in weight and, probably, cost. At best, protection against specialized anti-armour weapons can be provided only on a given aspect, say, the frontal arc, of a vehicle; the determination of such an arc is based on the probability of attack from a given direction, based on previous battle experience and Intelligence on the

tactics favoured by likely enemies and the weapons in use by them. Modern weapons and methods of attack, together with analyses of the Indo-Pakistani war and the various campaigns in the Middle East since 1945 have meant a complete re-think of the previously standard principles of armour distribution round an AFV; where previously the frontal arc of some 60° was considered the most important and vulnerable against specialized anti-armour weapons, the advent of 'smart' and top-attack missiles and the attack helicopter have meant that attack is liable to come from any direction. The implications of this are currently under urgent study, but few results of these studies have yet been seen.

One possible alternative to compound armour as an 'add-on' method of beating the HEAT projectile has recently been developed by the Israeli, and copied by the Soviet Army; this involves the explosive disruption of the incoming projectile by means of what is known as reactive armour. Known as 'Blazer' by the Israelis, reactive armour consists of packets containing a layer of explosive sandwiched between two metal plates which are hung around a vehicle's more vulnerable

► The new Soviet MBT T-80 fitted with reactive armour on turret and glacis plate. Note also the flexible 'skirts' protecting the lower nose plate. (MoD)

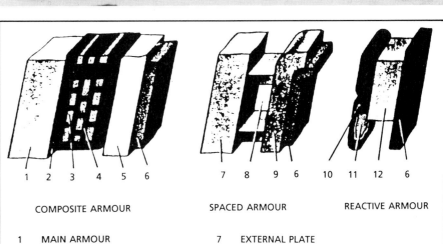

1 2 3 4 5 6	7 8 9 6	10 11 12 6	
COMPOSITE ARMOUR	**SPACED ARMOUR**	**REACTIVE ARMOUR**	

1	MAIN ARMOUR	7	EXTERNAL PLATE
2	SPECIAL ARMOUR	8	SPACE
3	CERAMIC TILES	9	INTERNAL PLATE
4	SUPPORT MATERIAL	10	REACTIVE ELEMENTS
5	SECONDARY ARMOUR (ANTI–SPALL)	11	EXPLOSIVE
6	ANTI–RADIATION LINING	12	MAIN ARMOUR

SOVIET IDEAS ON COMPOSITE, SPACED AND REACTIVE ARMOUR (MoD)

armour surfaces. When struck by the jet of a shaped-charge, the explosive detonates, driving the plates apart; their motion disturbs the HEAT jet, thus reducing considerably its ability to penetrate the armour of the vehicle. It is claimed that the addition of explosive reactive armour to a tank's existing steel armour raises the protection level against HEAT attack to at least three, and in some cases five times that given by homogeneous steel armour of the same weight. It was first used by the Israeli Army in the Lebanon in 1982, to protect their M60A1 and Centurion tanks; it has since been applied to the Merkava, has appeared on some Soviet tanks and has been tested on M60A1 tanks in the USA. As a means of protection against the emerging threat of attack from above, by homing sub-munitions, top-attack missiles and helicopters, explosive reactive armour seems likely to provide a more practical solution than either thicker homogeneous steel or compound armours. Its use on lighter vehicles is, however, limited by their inability to withstand the explosive shock, a limitation applying also to its employment near sensitive optical instruments. Once detonated, a reactive armour packet must be replaced if continued protection is required in that area; it is essentially a single-shot device. The reactive armour

principle also holds out the possibility of being connected to a threat detection system, which could detonate the packet in the area likely to be hit by an incoming missile before the missile had reached the correct stand-off distance for proper functioning; such a system would be known as an active system, and would have a greatly improved anti-HEAT performance over the reactive type. The technology for detection and initiation already exists; the main problem is likely to be cost.

Several modern armies prefer speed and agility to armouring against specialized weapons as the primary means of enhancing the capability of their tanks to survive. This is, to some extent, an emotional choice, but the logical case for it rests on:

1. The probable neutralization of a tank from the secondary effects of a strike, even if the primary effects are defeated.
2 The economic and logistical advantages of reducing the weight of the MBT by, say, 40 per cent.

The principal argument against reliance upon speed is that, especially in the direct fire zone, the tactical situation and the going will often preclude its use. Against KE attack, no conceivable target speed will

◄
A typical full-width anti-tank mine, in this case the British Bar Mine. This can be fuzed in a variety of ways, and is a very effective tank stopper. (ROF)

significantly reduce the chance of a hit, although a reduction in time of exposure to enemy fire may on occasion prevent a shot being fired. Against gun-delivered chemical energy attack, high target speeds will reduce the chance of a hit significantly but not dramatically, but against sub- and trans-sonic anti-tank guided-missile attack, high target speed and agility will often preclude the completion of an engagement within the time that the target is exposed and will also reduce the chance of a hit. Methods of attaining high speed and agility have already been discussed in the previous chapter; in general, they are an effective counter to first- and second-generation anti-tank GW but not to gun-delivered projectiles.

Gun and missile attack with specialized anti-armour projectiles employing chemical or kinetic energy to achieve penetration are not the only forms of attack against which an AFV requires protection. The anti-tank mine remains one of the tank's greatest enemies, and recent innovations in fuzing and mine-laying have increased its potential effectiveness against the very mobility which remains one of the tank's greatest assets.

Three types of mine attack must be considered:

1. The conventional high-explosive mine with a simple or double impulse fuze, exploded under the track or wheel and relying on blast to achieve its effect.
2. The conventional mine with a remote or 'multi-click' fuze, bursting under the vehicle's belly or its weaker rear end.
3. The shaped-charge or HEAT mine, remotely fuzed to burst under the belly; a variation of this is the HEAT *fougasse* or automatically fired rocket, which will attack the vehicle's side.

If damage to the track or wheel station is accepted, as it must be, there is no great difficulty in protecting against the conventional mine. Wherever possible, the main hull side plates are sloped downwards and inwards at about 5° to the vertical to direct the blast from a track- or wheel-detonated mine outwards away from the hull; great attention must also be paid to structural stiffness of the belly when designing the vehicle. Internal components and fittings are not mounted directly on to the belly plate but on sub-frames, which in turn are mounted on the hull side plates and bulkheads. With MBTs, it is also usual to reinforce or thicken the forward part of the belly under

the driver, and this also contributes to the structural strength of the hull against ballistic attack.

With more sophisticated fuzing systems, even mines that burst under the rear belly are unlikely to cause serious damage, provided that the crew are harnessed and components are mounted clear of the belly. Against belly attack from shaped-charge mines, however, it is quite impossible to protect, and crew casualties will invariably be high under these circumstances. The belly of a vehicle covers a large area, and normal ground clearance provides a convenient and ready-made stand-off distance. Normal protection against ballistic attack will work equally well against side attack from remotely fuzed shaped-charge devices, but against the belly this type of attack will have a devastating effect. Sophisticated fuzing systems employ silicon chips in complex electronic sensor systems which include double- or multiple-impulse devices, to defeat mine clearance rollers or to attack an AFV in, say, the middle of a column passing through a defile, in order to block the defile while defeating in detail the first vehicles past the mine. Other types of fuze operate on the magnetic influence of a metal-hulled AFV, or on the heat, sound or the ground vibrations emitted by it, and incorporate anti-handling and anti-lifting mechanisms; electronic fuzes have the advantage of being easily activated and de-activated remotely, thus enabling them to be lifted and used again. Many modern mines are undetectable by the normal electronic mine-detector, being made entirely of plastic; this characteristic, coupled with the sophisticated electronic fuzing systems and the mechanical laying devices now available, makes them a growing menace to the modern AFV.

One of the worst consequences of successful ballistic or mine attack on an AFV is fire; fire has been a weapon of war since time immemorial and 'We're on fire!' is one of the most dreaded warnings that can be heard by any AFV crewman. Ballistic attack of armour, whether by kinetic or chemical energy, generates great heat, and an AFV, by its nature, contains many substances, such as fuel and ammunition propellant, that are highly flammable when exposed to very high temperature. Special measures have to be taken, therefore, to protect AFVs against fire, particularly in ammunition stowage and engine compartments. British analysis of AFV crew casualties in 1943 showed that some 40 per cent of the total had been caused by burns; that fire suppression had not kept pace with AFV design was shown by Israeli reports on tank casualties sustained by their crews in the 1973 Arab-Israeli conflict, showing that, on the Israeli side alone, some 700 burn casualties were incurred during only eighteen days of fighting. With AFVs the fire risk is ever-present, but only materializes in peacetime through accident, misuse or bad crew discipline.

The main fire threats in an AFV are:

1. Ammunition, particularly propellant.
2. Fuel, lubricants and hydraulic fluid.
3. Rubber. This is slow to ignite and, except for roadwheel tyres, usually ignites from other fires. Burns very hot and difficult to extinguish.
4. Stowage. Bedding, camouflage nets and bivouacs are usually stowed externally. They are best stowed in bins, where oxygen to aid combustion is limited.

The risk of a fire can obviously be reduced by keeping the vehicle interior clean and free from oil, grease, rags and spilt fuel; care must also be taken by both day and night to ensure that, during refuelling, none is spilt either inside the vehicle or over external stowage. Not only must all electrical components near the fuel fillers be switched off, but they and the vehicle itself must be earthed to eliminate sparking from static electricity; these precautions must be a standard drill for AFV crews in both peace and war.

As a result of their experience during the Second World War, the British carried out much research after the war into AFV fire prevention and suppression, of propellant fires in particular. It was felt that, partly because of the fact that ammunition was stowed in the fighting compartment and partly because it was more easily ignited by splinters striking the cartridge case than was fuel by splinters penetrating the fuel tank, ammunition rather than fuel fire prevention held out the greater hope of reducing crew casualties. While ammunition continues to be hand-loaded by a crewman in the turret, the obvious option of stowing it outside the fighting compartment is not available; safer methods of stowing it internally had therefore to be found. British research showed that propellant ignition was caused by the heat generated when fragments of shell or armour penetrated the brass cartridge case, but that, if water could be injected immediately into the penetration, fire was suppressed; in addition, if the metal cartridge case were eliminated, by the use of a bagged charge and separate ammunition, the fire risk was still further reduced. It was also found that

ammunition stowed above the turret ring was more likely to be hit than when stowed in the hull. It has since become a British requirement that propellant shall not be stowed above the turret ring in AFVs.

First for Chieftain and then for Challenger, therefore, separate ammunition, using bagged charges contained in combustible cloth, was selected. Each charge is stowed in an individual inner container with a tight-sealing lid, and a group of inner containers is surrounded by an outer one. The space between inner and outer containers is filled with liquid, containing a smothering agent, under pressure; the simplest agent is water pressurized with carbon dioxide (CO_2), or, in lay terms, high-pressure soda-water! If a splinter penetrates the inner container, a jet of water follows it in, cooling it and smothering the fire instantly.

The Americans have opted for a different solution in the Abrams MBT. In this tank, ready rounds of ammunition are stowed above the turret ring in the turret bustle, in a compartment separated from the fighting compartment by an armoured bulkhead; should there be a hit on the ammunition in this compartment, the top is arranged so that it will blow off under pressure, and the explosion will thus be vented harmlessly away from the crew. Remaining ammunition is stowed in protected boxes in the hull, behind sliding armoured doors. In the event of a fire, an automatic Halon extinguishing system reacts within three milliseconds and extinguishes fires within two-tenths of a second.

British and other tanks also have built-in fire-fighting equipment, as well as carrying hand extinguishers for both internal and external use. The traditional method of extinguishing a fire in the engine compartment of a tank has been to stop the engine and discharge carbon dioxide from pressurized containers into the compartment. This is effective provided that the engine is stopped before the extinguishers are discharged, but the vehicle must halt and the engine is difficult to restart if carbon dioxide is still present. To extinguish a fuel fire without stopping the engine, essential when under flame-thrower attack, a liquid agent in droplet form must be used; the discharge arrangements have to be such that a film is deposited on all surfaces before the agent is swept out of the compartment by the cooling air. Such systems, employing an agent known as **BCS**, have superseded carbon dioxide systems on British tanks. A fire warning system that will operate reliably under all circumstances is, of course, essential.

The British and the Germans use the Graviner 'Fire Wire' system, which consists of fine stainless steel capillary tubing containing a fine, temperature-sensitive wire element, which is laid in both the engine and transmission compartments.

Hydraulic systems in the turret add appreciably to fire risk in AFVs, and for this reason (among others) are not permitted in British AFVs; powered traverse and elevation systems must be electric in their vehicles, and this is no hardship in these days of advances in electronic control systems. Other countries, such as the USA and West Germany persist with electro-hydraulic systems, however, despite their other disadvantages of greater weight and bulk. The trend is nevertheless towards all-electric systems, so that the fire risk from turret hydraulic systems should gradually disappear.

While there is currently no known method of completely suppressing propellant fires in tanks, the measures described above, both singly and in combination, will nevertheless help to reduce their incidence. Fuel fires are another matter, however, and as fuel fires can lead to ammunition fires it is an excellent reason for taking active measures to defeat them. The Halon system used in the US Abrams points the way; in lay terms, Halons extinguish fire by attacking its chain reaction, but their disadvantage was their toxicity, especially in confined spaces, when in contact with hot metal. The discovery of Halon 1301, however, eliminated the toxicity problem; this compound, when harnessed to a reliable detection, warning and control system, starts attacking the fire within 10–15 milliseconds of the release signal being generated and will completely extinguish a fuel fire within 60–100 milliseconds through only two outlets in the crew compartment. The cost of a complete Halon crew and engine compartment protection system is only some 0.8 per cent of total vehicle cost, and this is a small price to pay for saving a fully trained crew and their highly expensive tank. The West German and Dutch Armies have opted for Halon fire-suppression systems on their Leopard MBTs, and it is likely that all tanks of the next generation will be so equipped.

It is not, however, only against ballistic and mine attack, and the fires which can result from them, that the AFV crew requires protection nowadays and in the future; the three forms of attack grouped under the heading of NBC (Nuclear, Biological and Chemical) are very potent threats, all having the potential to knock out the AFV crew behind their armour, and nuclear attack having the additional threat of destroying the vehicle's electrical, optical and electronic systems, as well as the vehicle itself under certain circumstances.

The chemical, or gas, threat has existed as long as the tank itself, having been first employed by the Germans on the Western Front during the First World War. The chemical agents used then were dispensed from pressurized cylinders in the front line when the wind was blowing towards the enemy lines, and the wind was relied upon to disperse the gas over the enemy; they were either blistering agents, such as mustard, first used in 1917, agents operating against the lungs and respiratory tract or lachrimatory gases. The respirator was effective against the last two categories, provided it was fitted correctly and worn before the gas reached the wearer. Against mustard gas, however, the respirator served only to protect the face and respiratory tract of the wearer, the remaining exposed parts of the skin being vulnerable to the droplets of gas falling upon them; these droplets caused severe blistering and incapacitation wherever they came into contact with the skin, while where they fell on the ground they remained there to contaminate anyone later coming into contact with it. For this reason, mustard was known as a persistent gas.

As far as tank crews were concerned, their main threat came from the gases that attacked the respiratory tract; tanks of that period were very leaky objects and provided countless points of entry for such substances. Provided, however, that the gas cloud was detected in time for respirators to be donned by the crew, no particular damage was done; mustard, on the other hand, could be survived without respirators provided that all hatches were closed to prevent droplets falling on the crew. It was when the crew dismounted from a tank that had been contaminated by mustard that the problem arose whenever they touched exposed parts; the gas persisted until the vehicle was decontaminated back in unit lines by thorough scrubbing with plentiful supplies of water from powerful hoses, and special decontamination cream.

Although, from the military standpoint, chemical weapons had been proved highly effective, from the political standpoint they are eminently distasteful. They aroused extreme negative emotions throughout the civilized world, with the result that the Geneva Protocol of 1925, prohibiting their use, was agreed almost universally; despite this, there have been several

◄
The current standard British NBC suit, the Mk 4 Protective Oversuit, and S6 respirator. The oversuit is air permeable in one direction, to allow evaporation of perspiration. (HQ UKLF)

well-documented uses of toxic gases in military operations subsequent to its signing, notably by the Italians against the Ethiopians in 1935–6 and by the Japanese against the Chinese in 1937–42.

Although both Allied and Axis powers took defensive measures against possible enemy use of chemical weapons, and were making and stockpiling chemical agents during the Second World War, their use was limited to flame weapons, incendiary bombs and protective smokes. This was as well, for, in the occupation of Germany at the end of the war, Allied investigators discovered large stocks of three completely new agents for attacking the central nervous system, as well as the plants for manufacturing them; these agents, known collectively as nerve gases and individually as Tabun, Soman and Sarin, were closely allied to insecticides of the DDT type, which at that time was being produced in large quantities in the USA and Britain, and the smallest drop on the skin or aerosol droplet inhaled would cause almost instantaneous death from asphyxia due to paralysis of the central nervous system. Obviously, such agents represented a great jump in efficacy and lethality, against which the then current respirators and anti-gas clothing offered no protection; urgent steps were therefore taken in all the former Allied countries to find protection against, and an antidote to, these gases.

For the NATO allies, the problem was made the more urgent as not only had the Russians dismantled the German nerve gas factories and rebuilt them in the Soviet Union, but they were producing nerve agents and stockpiling weapons filled with them, in large quantities. Urgent action was accordingly taken to design, develop and issue protective clothing which covered the whole body, new respirators which would filter out nerve gas, self-injectors with which individuals contaminated by nerve gas could inject atropine to counteract its effects and detectors able to detect minimal quantities of nerve gas in the atmosphere and warn of their presence. AFVs were equipped with over-pressure systems, by means of which the interior could be kept at a pressure slightly above that of the air pressure outside when the vehicle was closed down, thus preventing the ingress not only of chemical and bacteriological agents but also of radioactive dust, and water when the vehicle was deep wading. Despite Soviet protestations that their resources devoted to chemical warfare are for defensive purposes only, and denials that they possess an offensive chemical warfare capability, their leaders have, when assailing NATO chemical and biological warfare measures, implied that the Soviet Union would at least give as good as it gets; the second half of the 1970s therefore marked the beginning of an upsurge in chemical defence activity on the part of the major NATO nations which has resulted in the current inventory of anti-chemical agent equipment.

For vehicle decontamination, both British and US equipment consists of a pressurized container, akin to a soda-syphon, charged with a decontaminant, to which is attached a hose and car-wash brush, issued on a scale of one per vehicle. For personal decontamination, both British and US troops are issued with Fuller's Earth dispensers in either pad or powder form. For the past twenty years or so, British AFVs have been fitted with collective NBC protection equipment; this consists of a central air intake and filtering system, to which each crewman's position is connected by flexible hose, into which the individual respirator can be plugged. The US has introduced similar equipment.

Biological or bacteriological warfare (BW) can be countered in AFVs by similar countermeasures to those taken against CW; its effects are slower acting and more long-term than those of CW, particularly nerve gas, and it is a threat which, luckily, has not so far materialized, as far as we know. The greatest danger arises when crews are dismounted; the greatest care has to be taken by them when remounting, to prevent the introduction of agents to the inside of the vehicle, as this is extremely difficult to decontaminate effectively. Some intake of agent or dust into the engine compartment is unavoidable, and this compartment therefore has to be sealed from the crew compartments. The positive pressure ventilation system is completely effective in protecting the crew against biological as well as chemical agents.

The future lies in the development of more sensitive detection devices, better antidotes to nerve gases and BW agents, more effective decontaminants for men and vehicles and more fightable masks and clothing.

The third component of the NBC trio is a relative newcomer, having only been developed during, and used in the last days of the Second World War; this is the nuclear weapon, whose effects are both immediate and residual. Immediate effects are those of blast, heat and nuclear radiation; residual effects are those of fallout, leading to radio-active ground and radio-active dust particles.

To deal first with the immediate effects, blast is likely to strip external fittings, including radio antennae and stowage, and may overturn the vehicle itself; obviously, the nearer the vehicle is to ground zero, the point of detonation, the worse will be the damage. For AFVs, blast is the 'governing effect', or the effect which does significant damage at the greatest distance from GZ, for weapon yields above 150 KT (kilotons); for yields less than this, immediate radiation becomes the governing effect, causing the crew to become quick casualties to greater ranges than the range at which blast will seriously damage the vehicle. The AFV's normal armour will protect the crew from the worst effects of blast, provided that the vehicle is closed down, and will also give a measure of protection against immediate radiation; of the many types of immediate radiation only gamma and neutron radiation are militarily significant. The attenuation of gamma radiation depends on the thickness and density of the protective material or, put another way, on the weight of material through which it must pass; for the absorption of neutrons, on the other hand, hydrogenous material such as polythene or hydro-carbon fuels, preferably incorporating an element with a high neutron capture capability, such as boron, would be required.

When considered in conjunction with structural strength, one is therefore led towards a sandwich arrangement of compound armour, having the main steel armour on the outside, a thin inner shield of steel and, sandwiched between them, a layer of boronated polythene or some other hydrogenous material. The Soviet Union is apparently the only great power so far to have adopted a metallized polythene liner, using lead rather than boron as the metallizer.

Ideally, protection against immediate radiation effects should be such that, against a typical low-yield weapon, one of the other immediate effects, either blast or thermal radiation, becomes critical. In a conventional tank, the weight penalty in achieving this is in the region of 10–15 per cent of the overall weight of the basically armoured tank; if one adds another 40 per cent for protection against specialized anti-armour CE and KE weapons plus the further 15 per cent for protection against immediate radiation, a basically armoured 35-tonne tank ends up weighing 56 tonnes. Such an increase puts the tank's weight above the generally acceptable limit, and other, less conventional tank layouts, involving fewer crew members contained in a single heavily protected hull pod or compartment, begin to find favour.

Immediate thermal radiation from a nuclear burst is unlikely to ignite paint or rubber at distances greater than those at which the effects of blast or nuclear radiation are predominant. It will set fire to flammable external stowage at ranges at which the other two principal effects are comparatively minor. Flammable items of external stowage should therefore be carried in bins. Flash is the other component of thermal radiation, in and around the visible waveband; since the intensity of this radiation is increased some 30–50 times by the characteristics of a tank's optical instruments, flash will damage both instrument and eye at very great ranges. For this reason, some form of instantaneous automatic shutter, preferably self-resetting, must be incorporated in the more important instruments, others being blacked out by manually operated internal shutters when there is a nuclear threat. The Kerr cell is one of several suitable shutter devices, triggered by the initial radiation and operating in the small but finite interval before the flash reaches full intensity. Night vision instruments will be put out of action by the flash, but will have ceased to transmit before permanent damage is inflicted on the operator's eye.

Finally, the remaining important immediate effect of a nuclear explosion is the pulse of electro-magnetic radiation emitted, known as EMP. This EMP has a catastrophic effect on electronic systems and sensors if steps, which are very costly, are not taken to protect, or 'harden' them against it. Little has been published on the effects of EMP so little can be said here about methods of combating it, but it must always be borne in mind when considering electronic equipment designed for installation in AFVs.

Against fallout and residual radiation, an AFV is inherently protected by its steel armour and its central positive-pressure ventilation and filtration system. Only two types of residual radiation are militarily significant, namely gamma and beta; only on the immediate fringes of a nuclear ground-burst area is gamma radiation likely to be a hindrance to AFVs, so that any vehicle leading a column needs to carry a dose-rate meter. An AFV's steel armour gives sufficient protection against the beta emissions from residual radiation and fallout.

A final type of attack under the generic heading of NBC, and the particular heading of CW, is that from

This illustration of the Soviet T-72 MBT shows clearly the smoke grenade-launcher tubes on the turret. They are so angled as to produce a rapid and continuous screen at a fixed distance from the tank, to enable it to move to a secure position under cover from enemy observation and fire. MoD)

flame-throwers. Protection from flame attack involves ensuring that nothing flammable is stowed on the outside of the vehicle, that all hatches are closed and the NBC protective system is in operation; providing these measures are taken, flame attack is far less dangerous to an armoured vehicle than might be expected. The engine must be kept running and the vehicle kept moving, so that a fire-extinguishing system of the surface-coating type, as mentioned earlier in this chapter, is essential for the engine compartment.

A defensive weapon also coming under the heading of CW, used for the protection of AFVs from observation, is chemical smoke. This comes generally in two forms, screening smoke and local smoke. Screening smoke is generally fired from guns at enemy positions, at ranges from 400 metres upwards, to screen off the enemy and prevent his observation of, and reaction to the tactical movements of one's own troops on the battlefield. Special smoke-projectiles are provided for all guns of about 75mm calibre and larger, including tank guns, and to build up an effective screen requires the firing of many rounds, as well as wind from the right direction. Such a screen will require to be thickened at intervals to ensure its continued effectiveness.

Local smoke, as its name implies, has a very local and immediate effect, and is used to conceal the move to cover of an AFV which has been observed and engaged by the enemy. It is a one-shot multi-launcher system, designed to cover the frontal arc of the turret; it can therefore give an effective short-term screen to the vehicle in any direction from which it is threatened,

by slewing the turret towards the enemy position. First used by the Germans on the Tiger and Pz Kpfw III tanks of their heavy tank battalions in the Second World War, the idea was copied by the British for the Centurion and all their later MBTs and has now been adopted by virtually all countries. Prior to the adoption of the multi-barrelled smoke-discharger, the British had employed a single-barrel 2in bomb-thrower loaded and fired from inside the turret, while the USSR used oil injection into the tank's exhaust to produce a screen of smoke; the problem with this last method was that the tank laying the screen tended to be visible at the head of it, virtually pin-pointed by the screen.

Protection from detection and observation is a very important category of protection, for all AFVs. Strategic deception plans play their part in this, but, at the tactical level, it is the responsibility of individual units and vehicle crews to protect themselves as far as possible from detection. Camouflage has always played its part in the obtaining of tactical surprise in battle, and in the days prior to the First World War and the introduction of aerial photographic and visual reconnaissance, was a comparatively simple matter of moving, where possible, by night and blending into the background by day. This was achieved by wearing dull-coloured uniform and removing items of metal such as cap badges which could reflect the sun's rays, as well as by covering the hard outlines of headgear with tree branches. Steps were also taken to deaden the sounds emitted by a marching column at night, such as by wrapping jangling buckles and other metal objects in cloth.

The advent of aerial reconnaissance changed all this; while night movement was still possible, aerial photography could detect it by the use of flares, and very strict drills had to be enforced during such movement in consequence, in an attempt to avoid discovery. Forming-up areas occupied by troops prior to an attack were the subject of elaborate deception plans to mislead the enemy as to the strength, place and direction of an attack.

The introduction of active infra-red night vision devices and cameras late in the Second World War further curbed the possibilities for unobserved tactical movement of AFVs by night, and IR photography had a disturbing effect on traditional methods of individual vehicle camouflage. In the past, random or 'dazzle' patterns of colours found in the surrounding environment had been used to help objects such as tanks, ships, aircraft and defence installations to blend into their background; in order to enhance the effect, tanks were covered in camouflage nets garnished in local colours and with large quantities of branches and greenery from local trees. To the dismay of traditionalists, however, it was soon discovered that IR photography could not only distinguish between the background and objects painted and camouflage-netted to merge into it, but could also distinguish between live and dead vegetation; a tank camouflaged by these methods thus stood out from its background like a sore thumb. While, in the early days after the Second World War and for some years subsequently, the scale of issue of near IR observation and fire-control devices was not large enough to warrant the abandonment of the traditional methods of concealment as regards opposing ground forces, the use of IR photography by photoreconnaissance aircraft was on a scale where concealment from air observation by these methods was extremely difficult; only by hiding in, or in the shadow of buildings or under the dense tree cover of mature forests could avoidance of detection be guaranteed, and only then if sufficient care had been taken to hide the wheel or track marks at the point of entry.

The widespread introduction of passive night vision devices in the form first of image intensifiers and secondly of passive thermal imaging and line-scan systems operating in the far IR band means that movement by night is as easy, and as detectable, as by day. What this will mean in terms of AFV crew fatigue has yet to be fully assessed; it may well mean that AFVs in any future war will have to adopt a 2-crew system similar to that of nuclear submarines, each crew doing

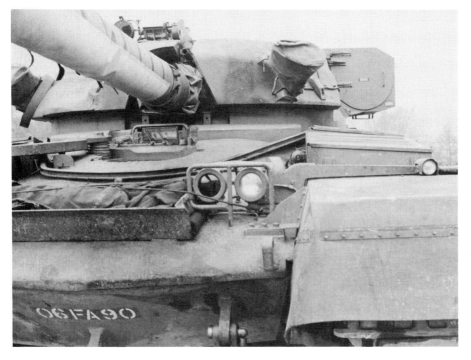

◀
In this photograph of a British Chieftain MBT with Stillbrew armour, the Near IR spotlight (behind the gun barrel) on the commander's cupola and one of the Near IR driving lamps can be seen. The main IR searchlight is in the box on the left of the turret. (HQ 1(BR) Corps)

a fixed period on and a similar period off duty. Apart from their effect on movement by night, thermal imagers can also be used with equal effect by day; relying as they do on the heat radiated by the objects in a scene, the differential heating pattern of an AFV is as easily detected behind cover by day as by night. The exhausts and engine compartment will be the hottest, unless the vehicle has been moving recently, in which case tyres, wheels and tracks will also show up hot, and these will show through camouflage, nets or natural, as if it were not there. The full implications of the introduction of thermal imaging on the conduct of tank movement, concealment and the gaining of surprise in war have yet to be fully assessed; they are very far-reaching and demand a radical rethink of methods of AFV concealment, from both ground and airborne passive heat detectors.

Ground surveillance radar is another detection system that has complicated the task of concealing a tank's movement from prying enemy eyes. Although an active system, which is therefore easily detected and can be put out of action by radar-seeking missiles, radar can see through fog, smoke, rain and mist better than any other observation aid; it is, however, unable to differentiate between static objects and the back-

ground, so is therefore limited to the detection of movement. Apart from the use of radar-seeking missiles against it, it is possible that AFVs finished in a suitably radar-absorbent paint might defeat detection by battlefield surveillance radar, but this is not yet more than a possibility.

The biggest problem for tactical commanders in a future war is going to be how to cope with passive Far IR and the thermal imaging and FLIR/Linescan aircraft equipments using these wavelengths; the effect of equipment in this category already in service on AFV concealment and movement, both by day and night, will be staggering, and the improved resolution and detection range of systems likely to be entering service in the 21st century will still further reduce the opportunities for the concealment and unobserved movement of armoured fighting vehicles and other military equipment in war.

Finally, an AFV crew needs to be protected against the effects of weather if it is to carry out its duties effectively under all conditions. Against the ingress of rain, sleet and snow, the sealing of hatches necessitated by NBC protection offers sufficient protection. Against the effect of cold, the electrically heated tank suit and gloves plugged into the vehicle supply suffices, while

▶
A British Spartan APC, a member of the CVR(T) family, mounting a ZB-298 battlefield surveillance radar on its roof. It can also easily be mounted on other wheeled or tracked reconnaissance vehicles. (Marconi Avionics)

excess heat can be counteracted by the vehicle's cooling fans. To protect against loss of visibility due to icing of, or heavy rain on observation and fire control instruments, their object glasses are provided with heaters, washers and wipers, as on civilian motor vehicles.

How then is armoured fighting vehicle protection likely to develop in the 21st century?

1. Against specialized anti-armour weapons Compound armour will continue to be used, possibly employing new materials, but every effort will be made to reduce the weight involved by reducing the volume requiring maximum protection. This is likely to involve dispensing with the conventional turret and housing a reduced crew in an armoured 'pod' in the hull.

Active systems of protection against in-coming sub- or trans-sonic anti-tank GW show promise, and could well be in service by the year 2000; the relatively low speed of the missile, its size and the low level of attack which will suffice to spoil the missile's terminal flight are all reasons why such a system shows promise and is technically entirely feasible. An operational system could consists of:

1. A detector, probably an elementary radar or IR sensor, capable of sensing a missile at 400–500m range, and of determining its azimuth angle of approach within a fairly wide arc.
2. A control unit capable of identifying the arc indicated by the detector and of operating the appropriate firing circuit.
3. Banks of grenade-launchers, similar to the present multi-barrel smoke-dischargers and with each bank covering an arc. Grenades should airburst and should deliver either instantaneous bursting smoke, to defeat the line of sight, or fragmentation/case shot, to spoil the missile's terminal flight, or a combination of the two.

Increased speed and mobility will be facilitated by the improved power/weight ratios and hydro-pneumatic suspension systems likely to characterize the tanks of the future; the crew pod system mentioned above will

help to lighten them and thus improve the power/weight ratio.

2. Against anti-tank mines The hull crew pod could be armoured all round, including the belly, with composite armour against shaped-charge mine attack, without incurring too great a weight penalty; however, it is difficult to imagine methods of protection against mine attack elsewhere on the vehicle other than by the use of specialist mine-clearance devices, vehicle-mounted or not. By breaking a track, blowing off one or more wheels or penetrating the engine compartment, a shaped-charge or simple blast mine will still stand a very good chance of immobilizing the vehicle.

3. Against fire The perfection of Halon or other extinguishing systems, including detection sensors and warning systems which will still further reduce the time interval between detection of a fire and its extinction, is to be expected, and the use of such systems will become universal on AFVs of the future. By their use, internal fires in AFVs should become a

danger of the past, particularly if combined with bi-propellant liquid in place of solid propellant for the main armament.

4. Against NBC attack The use of composite armours incorporating a neutron-absorbing inner liner will have become standard, and the abandonment of a rotating turret will simplify protection against all three types of attack by reducing the possible points of entry. The location of a 3-man crew in the hull will also simplify the provision and working of a central air filtration and conditioning plant. Improved chemical detectors for detecting the presence of nerve agents in the atmosphere are likely to have been developed, possibly working on the ionisation principle used by modern explosives detectors. At present, such detectors are relatively insensitive, slow to react and have a high false alarm rate; they do, however, have the advantage over present 'wet' chemical detector systems of being 'dry' and not requiring re-agent supply every twelve hours. There is no apparent reason why, using a micro-

◄
This group photograph of several current NATO MBTs shows, from left to right, the British Chieftain and Challenger, the FRG Leopard 2, the US M1A1 Abrams and the Vickers Mk 7. Their slab-sided similarity in appearance is due to their composite armour protection. (RAC Tank Museum)

123

processor to improve sensitivity and discrimination, such a system should not be working satisfactorily by the 1990s and be in service by the turn of the century, possibly in miniaturized wrist-watch form.

Against nuclear flash we can expect to see detectors and shuttering systems for optical instruments that will react more quickly than do those of today, giving complete eye protection to crew members using them. Against the EMP, hardening of affected electrics and electronics will be cheaper and accordingly more extensively used. The use of fibre optics will assist in this by replacing normal electric cable.

5. Against detection and observation It is in this category of protection that it is most difficult to see the way ahead into and beyond the year 2000. The present rate of acceleration in the development of optronics is so fast that it is difficult even to keep up with present developments, let alone to predict the course of future ones.

The biggest problem is presented by detection and observation devices operating in the Far IR band of the electro-magnetic spectrum; the increased sensitivity and target and image resolution capacity of future devices is likely to exceed by far the capability of present-day systems, which is already enough of a problem to those wishing to avoid detection. It is easy to think of the employment on a wide scale of thermal decoys and false targets, but, for these to be realistic, they will have to conform in size, shape and thermal characteristics to the items they represent; this presents a technical design problem as well as a logistic deployment and recovery problem. Another approach, at the vehicle design stage, is to keep the thermal gradient of a tank as flat as possible, reducing exhaust, engine compartment, track and road wheel temperatures as nearly as possible to that of the basic hull. The possibility of developing thermal camouflage nets, which can be thrown over a vehicle to level off the temperature gradient, needs to be investigated, as does the development of equipment to blind thermal imagers, rather on the lines of the visible-light CDL (Canal Defence Light) projectors developed by the British during the Second World War.

It is impossible to predict at this stage what the answer to the range of observation and detection equipment operating in the Far IR band of the spectrum will be in the 21st century, but one thing is certain; something will turn up, as it has always done in the eternal see-saw battle between offence and defence, attack and protection against it, to give the advantage back, if only temporarily, to the defence.

◄
A thermal image of a camouflaged Land Rover, photographed from the screen of a thermal imager. (British Aerospace)

GENERAL DESIGN

Geneeral design is that part of the armoured fighting vehicle design process concerned with the overall concept of the vehicle to meet the customer's requirement. Those of the design team who are responsible for general design are concerned with carrying out feasibility studies of new concepts, and with making the compromises necessary between the conflicting demands of the specialist designers responsible for the detailed aspects of AFV design such as armament, power plant, running gear, fire and gun control systems and armour. They are concerned also with ergonomics and anthropometrics and with working within the constraints imposed both by the customer's requirements and by the laws of physics, with the aim of designing a viable and functional vehicle that is easy to produce and operate and which is as cheap, light, powerful, agile, well-protected and reliable as possible. They will also assess carefully all new technical and scientific developments, for any possible relevance or application to AFV design.

The general design team will rarely, if ever, have an entirely free hand in the design of any AFV. The customer's requirements are paramount, and these will be based upon the role that the new vehicle will be required to fulfil. An armoured fighting vehicle exists solely as a means of giving mobility to the firepower it carries, while at the same time giving some protection to its crew. The relatively priority given to each of these characteristics of Firepower, Mobility and Protection in the customer's statement of requirements will depend entirely upon the role foreseen for the vehicle and will affect the general design of the vehicle accordingly. If, for instance, the vehicle's primary role is to be reconnaissance, priority in its design will be accorded to mobility; if, on the other hand the main purpose of the vehicle is to accompany and support infantry in the attack of fortifications and heavily defended positions, the primary design consideration could well be protection. A fundamental decision to be made, which will certainly be based upon the role of the AFV, is whether it should be wheeled or tracked. Not all armoured vehicles are capable of fighting and the purpose of these vehicles is to give mobility and protection to their load, which may be of fighting, maintenance or logistic personnel, rations, fuel, ammunition or spares; such vehicles are usually based upon the chassis of wheeled or tracked AFVs and are developed from them as a family of vehicles with commonality of parts and assemblies. Such variants of AFVs exist in such variety and numbers that only the basic fighting vehicles upon which they are, or are likely to be based will be discussed here.

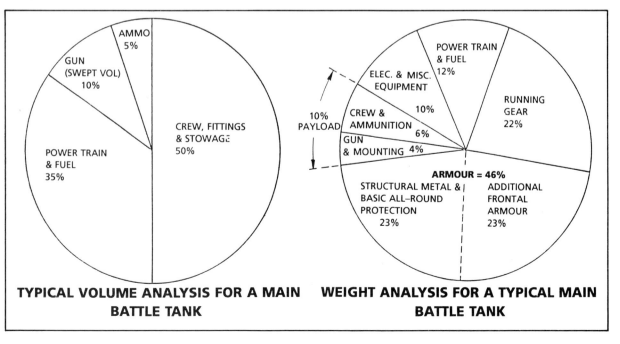

TYPICAL VOLUME ANALYSIS FOR A MAIN BATTLE TANK

WEIGHT ANALYSIS FOR A TYPICAL MAIN BATTLE TANK

125

Even when the customer's requirements are so vaguely stated as to impose a minimum of constraint on the designers, there are certain fundamental parameters concerning overall vehicle height, width, length and weight within which, if the vehicle is to be sufficiently mobile, the designers must operate. These parameters are a combination of those imposed by the requirement for the vehicle to be strategically mobile in and between theatres of war and those imposed by the laws of physics if the vehicle is to have tactical mobility.

For instance, the overall width and height permitted for the vehicle are laid down in the loading gauges of the railways over which the vehicle is likely to be transported. Maximum width, weight and ground pressure are limited by the portable bridging and other river-crossing equipment in service with the engineers or pioneers of the army for which the vehicle is being designed. The relationship between the width of a tracked vehicle and the length of its track on the ground (the steering, or L/C ratio) is fixed by the requirement for tactical mobility; a vehicle too long in relation to its width will be difficult, if not impossible to steer, while too short a vehicle will be directionally unstable. A steering (L/C) ratio of between 1.2 and 1.8:1 is the ideal aimed at by modern tank designers.

The weight of a tracked vehicle is exerted on the ground on which it is standing through its tracks, and it has been found from experience that, for a reasonable soft ground performance, a nominal ground pressure beneath the tracks of between 6 and 12psi is necessary; if the NGP is greater than 12psi the vehicle will be liable to become bogged in very soft going, while if it is less than 6psi it will lose adhesion in harder, hilly conditions. It will be obvious that the NGP will be a function of both vehicle weight and area of track in contact with the ground; with length of track on ground already derived from the steering ratio, the track area can therefore only be varied by means of the track width. Similarly with a wheeled vehicle, the weight is exerted on the ground through its tyres, and in this case the pressure exerted will depend on the number of wheels over which the vehicle weight is distributed, as well as on the width and radius of the tyres.

Apart from the limitation imposed by the rail loading gauge, vehicle height is directly affected by the considerations listed below:

1. The height of a standing loader.

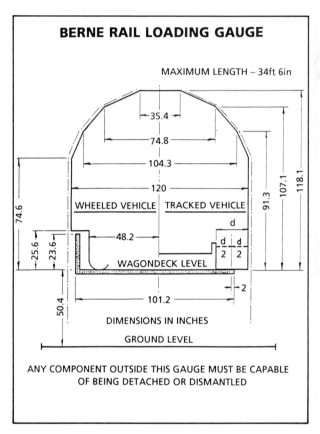

BERNE RAIL LOADING GAUGE

MAXIMUM LENGTH – 34ft 6in

WHEELED VEHICLE | TRACKED VEHICLE

WAGONDECK LEVEL

DIMENSIONS IN INCHES

GROUND LEVEL

ANY COMPONENT OUTSIDE THIS GAUGE MUST BE CAPABLE OF BEING DETACHED OR DISMANTLED

2. The recoil length of the gun in full depression.
3. The loading length of the longest round of ammunition.
4. The ground clearance specified by the customer.
5. The height of the power plant.

The fundamental relationships between certain dimensions already mentioned place certain constraints upon the vehicle design team; by far the greatest constraints, however, are those imposed upon the designers by the customer's requirements. These are generally stated in one of two forms by the General Staff of the army concerned; the first, known as a target, lists certain desired characteristics of function, dimensions and performance in general terms. The feasibility of combining these desired characteristics into a viable vehicle is then studied by the design team, who will generally issue one or more feasibility studies for consideration by the General Staff.

The second form in which requirements are stated is the General Staff requirement; this is a far more

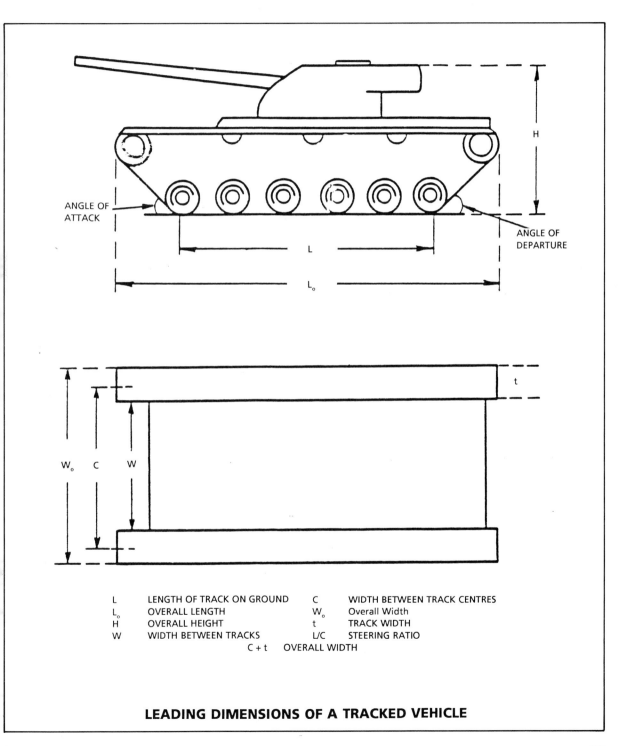

L	LENGTH OF TRACK ON GROUND	C	WIDTH BETWEEN TRACK CENTRES
L_o	OVERALL LENGTH	W_o	Overall Width
H	OVERALL HEIGHT	t	TRACK WIDTH
W	WIDTH BETWEEN TRACKS	L/C	STEERING RATIO
	C + t	OVERALL WIDTH	

LEADING DIMENSIONS OF A TRACKED VEHICLE

detailed specification of the vehicle's essential and desirable characteristics, based on analysis of the earlier feasibility studies, and the design team's response is a detailed design study accompanied by the construction of one or more full-size wooden mockups of the vehicle, for assessment by the ultimate user of the vehicle. In drawing up its requirements, the General Staff will have had before it as its main consideration the role for which the new AFV will be required. The general design of the vehicle will reflect the relative priorities given by the customer to firepower, mobility and protection, the three characteristics of an AFV already mentioned.

For example, when the requirement for 'Mother' was stated by the British during the First World War, the main role of the tank was to restore mobility to a battlefield on which the machine-gun, barbed wire and trenches had imposed a static war of attrition. Mobility and firepower were therefore the primary design criteria, with minimal attention given to protection. To this end, the specification called for a vehicle combin-

ing the ability to cross wide trenches and climb large vertical steps with firepower able to be brought to bear simultaneously on both sides of the vehicle and with protection from small arms ball ammunition and artillery shell fragments. The characteristic 'lozenge' shape of Allied heavy tanks of the First World War arose out of these requirements; to meet the trench crossing and step climbing requirement, 'Mother' was given overall tracks with a long length on the ground, and high front track wheels; so as not to outpace the accompanying infantry, she was given a maximum speed of 4mph, and the armour protection was sufficient to keep out ball but not armour-piercing ammunition. The main armament was mounted in sponsons on both sides of the hull to meet the requirement to be able to engage targets on both sides of the vehicle in the trench being crossed.

With mobility restored to the battlefield by the end of the war, the need for overall tracks and side-mounted main armament disappeared, and tank design generally changed as a result. The mounting of the main armament in a turret with 360° traverse carried on the hull roof and the use of half-round tracks became the norm, and greater attention was paid both to increased maximum speed and to increased armour protection. Experiments with auxiliary turrets were carried out, but these were found to be wasteful of crew as well as increasing vulnerability and size and were soon dropped; tank crews generally were reduced from the eight men in the British heavy tanks of the First World War to an average of five men. These were generally arranged so that the driver and co-driver/hull machine-gunner were accommodated in the hull while the commander, gunner and loader/wireless operator functioned from the turret. A fairly standard layout devolved, in which the hull was divided into three basic compartments; the front compartment, accommodating the driver and his controls together with the co-driver, if any, was naturally known as the driver's compartment. In the centre, carrying the turret and its crew, was the fighting compartment, while at the rear was the power plant and transmission in the engine compartment.

During the inter-war period, most countries gave higher priority to mobility and protection than to firepower, with the single exception of Germany, which gave firepower top priority. The role of the tank between the wars was, however, divided generally into

▲
A British Mk V tank of the First World War showing the typical 'parallelogram' shape, the overall tracks with long length on ground and the high front track wheel for trench-crossing and step-climbing. (Author's collection)

▶
British 'I' Tank Mk IV Churchill of the Second World War, heavily armoured, under-armed and with a multitude of small, individually sprung road wheels with little vertical movement. This suspension allowed only low speeds across country. (Author's collection)

◄ The British Second World War Crusader, a cruiser tank whose Christie-type suspension allowed large wheel movement and high cross-country speed. Like the Churchill, it was under-armed, the vehicle in the photograph mounting a 6pdr (57mm) main armament. (Author's collection)

▶ The British Centurion 'universal tank'. First user trials vehicles, armed with a 17pdr (76mm) gun, saw no action in Europe during the war, but it later performed well in service throughout the Western world. These Mk 3s are armed with the 20pdr (84mm) gun, and later Marks were up-gunned to 105mm. (MoD)

three distinct parts, for each of which a separate design of vehicle was required; these were, first, a heavy and heavily armoured vehicle to accompany the infantry in the attack (known in the British Army fairly logically as an Infantry or 'I' Tank); secondly, a lighter, more lightly armoured high-speed vehicle, known by the British as a Cruiser Tank, to exploit the breakthrough of enemy positions forced by the infantry tanks and accompanying infantry; and, thirdly, a very fast, light tank for reconnaissance. The vehicles designed to fill these roles had characteristics as varied as their roles; the heavy, slow infantry tanks gave highest priority to protection, followed by firepower and mobility in that order. The cruiser or medium tanks were designed with the greatest accent on mobility and firepower, with protection the lowest priority. The light tanks gave highest priority to mobility, with minimal attention paid to firepower and protection.

The outbreak of the Second World War soon revealed deficiencies in the tanks with which the Allies entered the war; without exception they were under-armed, and, in the case of the British cruiser and light

tanks, under-armoured as well. Anti-armour weapons proliferated, and a constant programme of up-armouring and up-gunning of tanks was maintained by both sides. The general design of tanks, however, remained true to the pattern established between the wars, at least as far as layout was concerned; gradually, however, the distinction between heavy infantry and fast medium or cruiser tanks became blurred as all tanks increased in both weight and firepower, until, by the end of the war, even the British General Staff was calling for one design of tank, the 'Universal Tank', to fulfil all tank roles. Since the Second World War, the hull MG, and hence the co-driver, has been eliminated, to give more internal stowage space, to allow the driver to be centrally placed in the hull and to permit of better ballistic shaping of the hull frontal armour. All countries with the exception of the Soviet Union appear finally to have decided that one tank can indeed fill all the tank's roles, as well as giving greater logistic and training simplicity, and have opted for the 'main battle tank' (MBT) solution; to such an extent that it is very difficult, especially for the layman, to distinguish

between British, US, West German, Italian, French, Korean and Japanese examples.

The battle between firepower and protection against it has been waged since time immemorial, with attack and defence alternating in having the advantage as new weapons, and new methods of protecting against them, were invented. Before the introduction of firearms, the cavalryman represented the optimum combination of firepower and mobility; with the advent of firearms, however, the cavalryman became vulnerable to foot soldiers at a range beyond the reach of his own weapons, and to have armoured him adequately against the firearm would have removed his mobility and hence his *raison d'être*. What is more, firepower continued to develop while mobility continued to be based on the horse, so that, by the outbreak of the First World War firepower had advanced so far beyond the then available means of mobility that these two essentials of offensive action could no longer be combined and operations, as we have seen, stagnated, turning into large-scale static battles of attrition as a result.

The standard means of protection for AFVs, in both World Wars as well as between them, was steel armour plate, homogeneous or face-hardened, rolled plate or cast; as the opposing anti-tank firepower was increased, both by increasing the calibre and muzzle velocity of kinetic energy ammunition and by the introduction of chemical energy projectiles using the shaped-charge or high-explosive anti-tank (HEAT) principle, protection against this improved ammunition was obtained by increasing both the thickness and the slope of AFV armour. As the chemical energy projectiles became more numerous, and as the correct functioning of this type of projectile depends on its detonation at a certain stand-off distance from the armour plate under attack, additional detachable spaced plates were placed in front of the main armour on certain tanks, in order to initiate the shaped-charge prematurely. By adding armour, both methods of protection meant an increase in the vehicle's all-up weight, and AFV weights in action began a remorseless rise which has continued ever since; at the outbreak of the Second World War, the average tank weighed some

▶
The West German Leopard 2, a good example of a current MBT showing the typical 'slab-sided' appearance imparted by composite armour. (Krauss Maffei)

20 tonnes in action, whereas, by the end of the war, this average weight had more or less doubled.

Since 1945, main battle tank weights have continued to rise; NATO MBTs now in service weigh from 50 to 62 tonnes, and approximately fifty per cent of this weight is taken up by armour protection. Not all of this protection nowadays is of homogeneous armour steel, however; exotic composite armour materials have been developed to counter the chemical energy HEAT weapon, and these are bulky, heavy and expensive. The HEAT projectile has developed to such an extent that the ratio between its diameter (calibre) and the thickness of steel armour that it can penetrate has increased from 3.5:1 to about 6:1; in other words, a rocket or a guided missile launched from an infantry position can penetrate more steel armour than it is

practicable to put on a tank if it is to retain its mobility. Anti-tank projectiles relying on their kinetic energy for armour penetration have also made great strides, to the extent that required penetration can be achieved with a reduction in gun calibre of some 30 per cent. Add to these difficulties to be faced by the modern MBT the threat posed by the superior speed and mobility of the anti-tank helicopter and fixed-wing aircraft firing 'fire and forget' anti-tank missiles with heat-seeking warheads to home on to the vulnerable warm engine compartment roof and it may be felt that the day of the heavy and expensive MBT is more or less over.

This will by no means be the first time that the end of the tank has been foreseen, neither will it be the last;

▼ **A typical three-compartment tank, the Soviet T-72.**

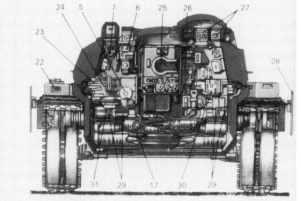

T-72 MEDIUM TANK

1. FG-125 HEADLIGHT
2. STEERING LEVER
3. NBC PROTECTION SYSTEM (PAZ)
4. GEAR SHIFTING LEVER
5. MANUAL ELEVATING MECHANISM
6. TPD2-49 RANGEFINDER AND SIGHT
7. TPN1-49-23 IR NIGHT SIGHT
8. ILLUMINATOR FOR TKN-3 SIGHT
9. NSVT ANTIAIRCRAFT MACHINEGUN
10. AMMUNITION CASSETTE LIFTING
    MECHANISM
11. ANTENNA
12. STORAGE BOX FOR SNORKELING
    EQUIPMENT (OPVT)
13. ENGINE
14. TRANSMISSION
15. AUXILLIARY FUEL TANK
16. PROJECTILE AND PROPELLANT CHARGE
    AN AUTOLOADER CASSETTES

17. AUTOLOADER
18. GUNNERS SEAT
19. CHEMICAL AGENT
    DECONTAMINATION KITS
20. DRIVER/MECHANICS SEAT
21. PARKING BRAKE
22. SPT AND A STORAGE BOX
23. MANUAL TURRET TRAVERSING
    MECHANISM
24. AZIMUTH INDICATOR
25. BREECH BLOCK
26. PKT COAXIAL MACHINEGUN
27. COMMANDER'S VISION DEVICES
28. PROTECTIVE SKIRTS
29. AMMUNITION BOXES FOR PKT
    MACHINEGUN
30. RADIO
31. POWER TRAVERSING MECHANISM

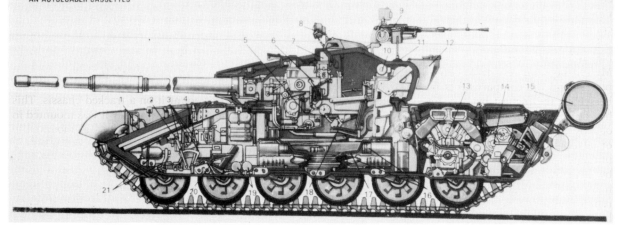

apart from the antipathy on the part of vested military interests to the very introduction of the tank in 1915, its end was forecast during the Spanish Civil War in the 1930s; in the middle of the Second World War when bigger anti-tank guns appeared; after the war, when rocket-launchers and recoilless guns appeared, and more recently when anti-tank guided missiles first came on the scene. This time, however, there is more justification to the claim, particularly if one modifies it to forecast the end of the MBT as presently configured. There is no doubt whatsoever that the present MBT is too heavy, too big, too difficult to maintain and too expensive; its expectation of life on the modern battle-field is likely to be very short indeed, and there is a feeling that, if not the next generation of MBTs then the one after will be lighter, smaller and, as a result, it is to be hoped, cheaper.

As we have seen, approximately 50 per cent of the weight of the modern MBT is due to its armour protection; any reduction in armour will therefore have a very beneficial effect on the overall weight of the tank, and it is in this direction that the designers of future MBTs will probably move. Modern methods of attack of armour mean that the armour can no longer be distributed over the vehicle in the proportions that have been customary in the past; attack is as likely to come from above, below or to the rear as from the front, which means not only that the thickness of armour in these areas must be increased but also that the angle which the armour presents to the frontally attacking projectile must be adjusted so that it presents a similarly difficult angle to attack from the new directions. This is impossible to do with the present configuration of MBT without an unacceptable reduction in its mobility, both strategic and tactical, so the configuration will have to change.

It is the volume needing to be armoured that is the biggest single cause of the excessive weight of current MBTs; the crew of a tank is its highest-valued component and the compartments occupied by its members have the highest priority for protection. A crew having fewer than the standard four members will occupy a smaller volume and hence require less weight of armour for the same level of protection. The ultimate in human crew reduction would be achieved by dispensing with it altogether, controlling the tank, manoeuvring it and bringing its firepower to bear by remote control; apart from the cost of such a solution, however, it would be unlikely to be viable in the fog of war, especially in an electronic warfare environment. The next best thing is to reduce the crew to essential personnel only; these would be the driver, to look after mobility, the gunner, to look after the firepower and the commander, to apply the overall tactical plan. By dispensing with the human loader and substituting an automatic one, not only is the crew reduced by one member, but that member, it will be remembered, is the one exerting most influence on vehicle height by the necessity for him to be standing in order to load the main armament. If, at the same time, the crew were to be removed from the turret to a driver's enlarged compartment in the hull it would be necessary to armour only the one crew compartment, thus effect-ing a further saving in weight; while dispensing with a conventional turret would save complication as well as weight, at the same time greatly reducing not only the backlash problems associated with conventional turrets, with their adverse effect on firepower accuracy, but also the electrical loads involved in stabilizing a turret in azimuth. The sealing of the crew compartment against the entry of chemical warfare (CW) or bacteriological warfare (BW) agents would also be greatly simplified.

The armament of future tanks poses some interesting questions; the tank has, over the years, increasingly become an anti-tank weapon, mounting a conventional long-barrelled gun which fires, as its primary ammunition, kinetic energy rounds of ever-increasing projectile weight and velocity. High-explosive anti-personnel ammunition is carried, but in smaller quantities and only as a secondary role. The primary reason for this role change can be traced back to the Second World War, when virtually the only available means of attacking armour was the high-velocity gun, firing projectiles which relied for their armour penetration on their kinetic energy; the calibre, barrel length and muzzle velocity were increased to such an extent that the towed anti-tank gun lacked the necessary mobility and manoeuvrability across country, and it was there-fore necessary to mount it on a tracked chassis. This was done in one of two ways; either it was mounted in a tank turret, with 360° traverse, or it was mounted in a tank hull, with only limited traverse, the resulting vehicle being known as a tank destroyer or self-propelled (SP) anti-tank gun. With the large tank gun calibres in use nowadays a very respectable high-explosive (HE) projectile can also be fired from the tank gun, but this was not always so; as far as the

◀
The greatest self-propelled tank destroyer of the Second World War, the German Jagdpanther, mounting a gun of 88mm calibre, 71 calibres long, with limited traverse in the modified hull glacis plate of the Panther tank. (Author's collection)

British were concerned, until the 75mm guns of the US Grant and Sherman were available, halfway through the Second World War, the 2pdr was too small and the 6pdr too unreliable as HE firing weapons.

However effective in the role, a modern MBT is a very expensive and not very cost-effective tank killer; where, for some years after the war at least until the late 1960s, a reasonably accurate rule of thumb for estimating the cost of a tank was £1,000 per ton, a modern MBT such as Leopard 2 or Challenger costs some twenty times this figure. While inflation accounts for some of this increase, by far the greater proportion (some 37–40 per cent of total cost) is due to the electronics now necessary for fire control and night vision systems. The kinetic energy projectile is by no means the only, or even the primary method of killing tanks since the introduction of the shaped charge, the man-portable rocket and the crew-portable anti-tank guided weapon (ATGW), although it must be acknowledged that both KE and chemical energy forms of attack are required if a potential enemy is to be kept guessing as to how best to protect his tanks against attack.

If, therefore, the weight and cost of the future tank are to be reduced to a figure affordable in the required quantities by a single country rather than a consortium of countries in co-operation, considerable thought must first be given to the role that this tank is expected to fill. Is its main function to continue as a tank-killer?

If so, should it use a gun or a guided rocket as its main armament? Rely on KE or chemical energy, or both, as its means of penetration? Use homing, guided or unguided projectiles? Have one barrel/launcher or multiple? Or should the main armament have more than one purpose, to continue to be used also as an anti-personnel weapon?

Answers to all these questions must be clear in the minds of the general design team before attempting to put pencil to paper; armies are, however, notoriously slow to accept new ideas and it is unlikely that the role of the MBT of the future will be radically changed in the early decades of the 21st century, however much the design may be changed to reduce weight, size and cost. This, then, implies that the main armament will continue to be a high-velocity gun firing both KE armour-piercing and HE ammunition; other forms of armour attack will be available from the helicopters, with which the tanks will co-operate closely, and the infantry. As far as armour-piercing performance is concerned, the gun will ideally be required to penetrate enemy armour at a range greater than that at which enemy tanks can penetrate the armour of its own vehicle. In this connection, the improvement in KE projectile performance given by the APFSDS long rod penetrator means that the NATO standard 105mm gun can ·now overmatch present armour combinations to the extent that the advantage of up-gunning to 120mm has virtually disappeared; in the cause of reducing tank weight and size, therefore, it would seem sensible to concentrate on the smaller calibre for future tanks.

The future tank of the early years of the 21st century can now be seen to be taking shape. With a maximum weight of 35–40 tonnes, it seems likely to carry a crew of three, to mount a 105mm gun as main armament and to concentrate the armour protection round a 'crew pod' rather on aircraft lines. It must not be forgotten that the tank's sole reason for existence is as a mobile platform for firepower, and it must be asked whether there are not now, or will not be, other means available of giving possibly increased mobility to firepower on the battlefield. Is, for instance, a means of mobility that is limited to contact with the ground ever likely to be able to give sufficient speed of movement to enable a vehicle to rely on hit avoidance rather than armour for its protection? We have seen that a vehicle relying on armour for its protection could never carry enough to guarantee its survivability against even the currently available spectrum of attack, so that an element of hit avoidance, implying greater agility and mobility than at present, will be necessary in addition to armour protection for the tank of the next generation.

For the generation after that, it could be that a very fast, light cross-country vehicle, possibly wheeled, and armoured only against smallarms fire and shell fragments but carrying an effective anti-tank weapon would suffice as a tank replacement; if not alone, then in conjunction with a vehicle, such as a helicopter, which, as it does not rely upon ground contact to obtain its mobility, will be capable of very much greater tactical agility and cross-country speed than any wheeled or tracked vehicle. Such a radical solution would, however, be accepted only with the greatest reluctance, if at all, by the reactionary elements in most armies of the world. The advantages of such a vehicle in cheapness, ease of training and maintenance, ease of production and tactical and strategic mobility need no emphasis; it is, however, still questionable whether a vehicle in contact with the ground could ever possess sufficient cross-country agility for it to be able to rely for protection upon hit avoidance alone. There is much to be said in favour of an airborne vehicle in this connection; it can take avoiding action in three dimensions instead of only two, and an anti-tank missile launched from the air can more easily attack the more vulnerable, and hotter, top plates of an AFV than one launched from the ground.

Reverting to the question of the armament of the next generation of tanks, likely to come into service before the end of this century but to remain in service through the first decade of the next, two crucial general design questions arise: first, does the gun need to have 360° of traverse independent of the hull and, secondly, does the gun need to be stabilized in azimuth, or elevation, or both?

It has been the convention since the First World War that the main armament of a tank or armoured car should be mounted, with its crew, in a turret capable of 360° traverse, so that targets can be engaged with minimal delay wherever they may be located. This arrangement, which has worked very satisfactorily until the present, nevertheless carries certain penalties:

1. The crew is divided between two compartments, both of which need armour protection.
2. The turret adds height and therefore weight to the vehicle.
3. The turret traverse mechanism is a source of backlash and therefore error in laying the gun.
4. The joint between turret and hull is vulnerable, and is difficult to seal against chemical and biological attack.
5. The electrical joint between hull and turret is a source of weakness in power supplies to the turret and a source of interference to radio communications.

Since the war, it has also been customary for the armament of an MBT to be stabilized, certainly in elevation but frequently also in azimuth, so that it can be fired with accuracy on the move. The loads and electrical power involved in attempting to stabilize an out-of-balance gun, the balance of which changes as it is fired and reloaded, are very large, and the system, whether it be electric or electro-hydraulic, to do the job is heavy and takes up much space (which is perforce armoured) in the turret. The loads involved in stabilizing so large and heavy an item as an MBT turret in azimuth are even greater, and add more bulk and weight to the overall stabilization system. The accuracy with which gun and turret can be stabilized have not, in the past, equalled the accuracy of the gun and sighting system, with the result that accurate fire from the moving tank has not really been possible; it has been possible only to keep the gun and sights in the vicinity of the target, the tank having to halt to engage the target accurately. The fact that the gun and sights have been kept in the vicinity of the target, however, enabled the tank to get off its first shot at the target very much more accurately than if the gunner had had to find, and lay his sights and gun on the target from scratch after the vehicle had come to a halt; speed of engagement is essential in tank warfare, and this could be the only justification for the sacrifice of precious armoured volume, weight and cost involved in the provision of gun and turret stabilization of such low efficiency.

The need to be able to fire on the move was foreseen from the start, and the sponson-mounted guns of the first tanks were shoulder-controlled by the gunner in elevation and manually in traverse; of course, traverse angles were limited and tank speeds low, which made the gunners' task feasible. After the introduction of the turret with all-round traverse, the gunner was provided

with a manually operated geared traverse mechanism, but continued to control the gun in elevation by means of his shoulder; however, as turret weights increased, traversing them required some form of power assistance, and power traverse mechanisms, either electric or hydraulic, became standard. During the war, gun calibre, length, weight and out-of-balance all increased to the point where shoulder control in elevation was no longer possible, and manually operated gear systems were universally introduced. The advent of the US M-4 Sherman as Lend-Lease equipment from 1943, however, changed both UK and Soviet thinking; the Sherman had a rudimentary gyro stabilizer applied to the gun elevation system, which enabled the gunner to fire on the move with at least some accuracy, and after the war both countries developed their own stabilization systems as a result. The British developed an

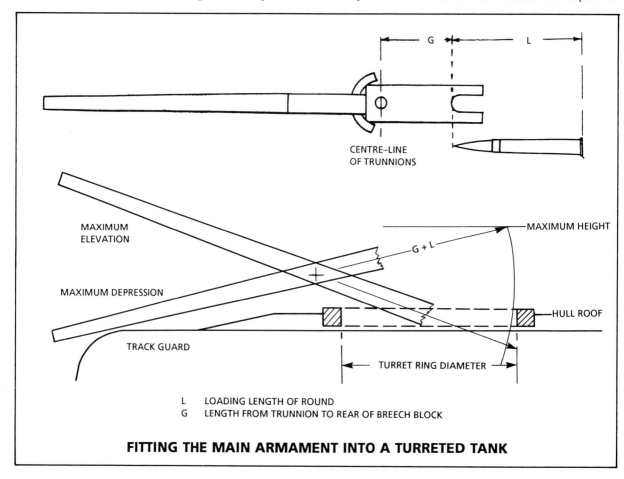

CENTRE–LINE
OF TRUNNIONS

MAXIMUM ELEVATION

MAXIMUM DEPRESSION

MAXIMUM HEIGHT

HULL ROOF

TRACK GUARD

TURRET RING DIAMETER

L   LOADING LENGTH OF ROUND
G   LENGTH FROM TRUNNION TO REAR OF BREECH BLOCK

FITTING THE MAIN ARMAMENT INTO A TURRETED TANK

electrical rotary metadyne system, which first appeared on the very successful Centurion MBT in 1945 and which provided gun stabilization in elevation and turret stabilization in azimuth. The Soviets did not attempt stabilization of the turret but limited their efforts to gun stabilization in elevation. Only the Americans, who had introduced stabilization in the first place, were not convinced of its efficacy and omitted it on their first post-war tanks. The British systems since, and including that of Centurion, have been all-electric in operation, reflecting British dissatisfaction with their wartime hydraulically operated systems; these were found to be very vulnerable to ingress of dirt in the North African desert, as well as adding considerably to the fire risk in a tank hit by enemy fire. Other countries, however, have preferred the smoother operation of electro-hydraulic systems and accepted the leaks of hydraulic fluid inherent with such systems, until the recent electronics explosion introduced the possibility of replacing rotary electrical machines and hydraulic servos with very compact and highly efficient solid-state drives.

The futility of attempting to stabilize the modern MBT turret in azimuth to anything like the accuracy required to enable the modern high-velocity tank gun to use its accuracy to the full from a moving tank has now been realized; how much easier just to stabilize the sight, with its small mass, to the right degree of accuracy, and to slave a roughly stabilized gun and turret to it electronically, so that the gun will fire only when the gunner's sight and the gun are aligned with it. Already the West German Leopard 2 and the US M-1 Abrams MBTs are employing this system with success, as the results of the Canadian Army Trophy NATO tank competition have shown; the French Leclerc is also to use a similar system.

It is obviously desirable that a tank should be able to deliver accurate fire while on the move, whether on roads or across country. There is therefore a requirement for stabilization, whether of sights alone, of sights and gun or of the complete turret, to a degree that will enable the full accuracy of the gun and ammunition to be utilized from a moving vehicle; the smaller the mass to be stabilized, however, the easier it is to achieve the accuracy required, the less volume is occupied by the stabilization system and the cheaper the system to do it will be. There is much to be said, therefore, for stabilizing the sight head to as great or greater a degree of accuracy as the sight/gun combina-

tion is capable of, and slaving the gun to it when a target is found; similarly, the smaller the mass to be slaved to the sight, the easier and cheaper it will be to do so. From the point of view of accurately firing on the move, therefore, the discarding of the conventional turret, its armour and its vulnerable and error-inducing traversing mechanism, and the relocation of the turret crew elsewhere in the vehicle is highly desirable; it will also have the advantage of reducing the height of the tank, its weight and its frontal silhouette in a hull-down firing position.

With so many obvious disadvantages, it may well be asked why the countries of NATO and the Warsaw Pact have retained the turreted tank in service for so long; the answer is that, until recently, there was no method by which the commander and the gunner could be given an adequate picture of the battlefield or of the target unless they were in the turret close to the gun and using conventional optical instruments to obtain it. With current multi-sensor optronic capabilities and the development of the optical slip-ring, it is now possible to mount the sensors near to the axis of the gun bore while transmitting the resulting image to a commander and gunner located remotely from the gun axis, say in the hull. The only problem remaining to be solved in such a measure is that of image resolution and acuity, and there is no reason to suppose that, with image enhancement techniques, this problem will not be solved well before the year 2000. One other possible problem arises with this type of system, in which the commander and gunner are located in the hull and facing in a fixed direction; it is one of disorientation, when the vehicle is travelling in one direction and the sight picture is covering another. Trials will be needed to show whether or not this is a real problem, or one that can be overcome with training or possibly drugs to counter motion sickness.

Having established the desirability of dispensing with the turret in the next generation of MBTs, let us examine the various possibilities of doing so; basically, these are either to mount the gun in the hull or to mount it externally, above the hull. A hull-mounted gun, while bringing the gunner nearer to the gun axis, has the disadvantage of restricting the gun's traverse independent of the hull as well as exposing more of the hull in a fire position on a reverse slope; to traverse the gun more than a few degrees, the whole vehicle must be turned. Only one tank mounting its gun in the hull has been brought into service since the war and that is

▶
The Swedish StrV 103B or 'S' Tank, a novel post-1945 solution to the problem of increasing height and weight in the turreted MBT. The gun is fixed in the hull and is traversed and elevated by moving the vehicle on its tracks, and hydro-gas suspension. (AB Bofors)

the Swedish 'S'-Tank, a technically advanced vehicle with many advantages for the primarily defensive role envisaged for it in the specific Swedish situation; its traverse system is, however, such as to make the engagement of moving targets difficult, and firing on the move impossible. Both the German and Soviet Armies have made use of many hull-mounted anti-tank guns in and since the war, but these were self-propelled tank destroyers rather than tanks; their limitations were offset by the fact that, weight for weight and tank chassis for tank chassis, a bigger gun could be mounted

than was possible in the turreted version of the tank whose chassis had been used as the SP mounting. Their tactical use was mainly defensive.

The other alternative, more suitable for a battle tank, is to mount the gun above and outside the hull, in a mounting which will give 360° traverse and is provided with an auto-loader. Such mountings have been examined many times since 1945, notably by the Swedish Army, but also by the British, West German and US Armies and others. The gun could be mounted on a pedestal, either of fixed height or raisable, with located within the rear hull armour. The fixed external mount proposal demands an externally-mounted auto-loader at the rear of the tank, adding to its vulnerability.

The form likely to be taken by the future MBT now becomes clearer; we have seen that it is likely to be turretless, mounting its armament externally above the hull on a pedestal which can be retracted when not in use and which gives the armament 360° of traverse and the specified elevation and depression arcs. The commander and gunner will be located in the hull and obtain their 'top' vision via optronic sensors, located near to the armament axis, which relay enhanced images of high resolution and acuity to the crew in the hull. The armament, and the gunner's sight, will be slaved to the commander's sight, which will be fully stabilized in both elevation and azimuth; both sights will have a full passive night vision capability, probably employing far IR thermal imaging.

In this discussion so far, it has been assumed that the future MBT of the 21st century will have a high-velocity gun as its main armament, but no reasons for this assumption have yet been given. The most important reason is the gun's ability to fire both kinetic energy and chemical energy anti-tank ammunition, as well as high-explosive anti-personnel rounds; the gun is cheaper per round to fire than the guided missile, has no minimum range and its projectiles, even those employing chemical energy, which require a lower striking velocity than KE, have a much shorter time of flight, thus giving the enemy target little time in which to take avoiding action. It is possible to stow more rounds of gun ammunition than guided missiles in a tank under armour, they are easier to load than missiles and they need less frequent and less complicated functioning tests. The disadvantage of the gun when employing HEAT ammunition is the limitation placed by the calibre of the weapon upon the cone diameter of the projectile, which, it will be remembered, largely dictates the thickness of armour that it can penetrate; the rotation imparted to its projectiles by the rifling of a gun barrel also adversely affects the penetration of HEAT projectiles. The preference of future tank users, therefore is likely to be for a smooth-bore gun as the main armament of the future tank generation.

Even with the redistributed armour protection of the future MBT, if it is to be as light as desired it will have to depend to some extent on hit avoidance for its

solid-state electric drives for traverse and elevation and carrying the optronic sensor heads for day/night vision and ranging; such a solution would greatly reduce the frontal area exposed in a hull-down position compared to that of a conventional turret. Of the two alternatives, the raisable gun mount has the advantage that, when not in use, the mounting is protected within the hull, while the gun could lie in a 'cleft' in the hull roof and glacis plate, thus also gaining some protection from flank attack; the mount could also be lowered for loading the gun from the auto-loader, which could be

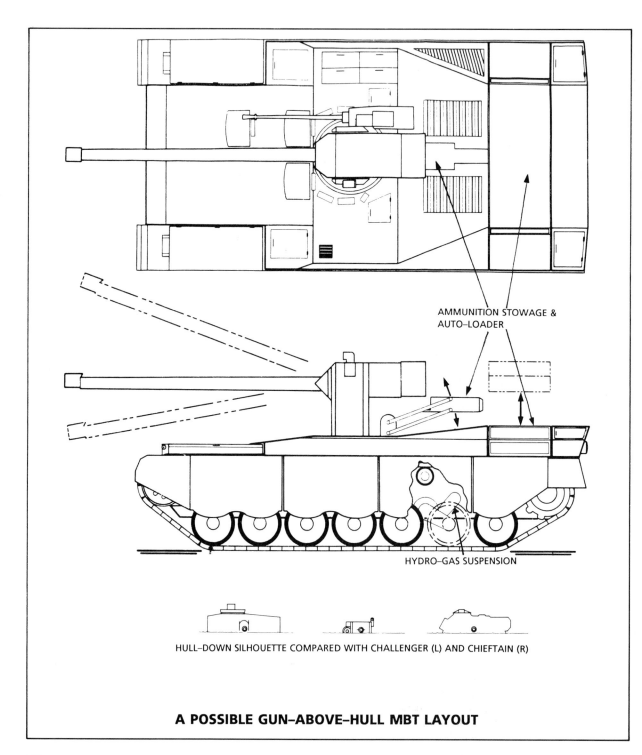

AMMUNITION STOWAGE &
AUTO–LOADER

HYDRO–GAS SUSPENSION

HULL–DOWN SILHOUETTE COMPARED WITH CHALLENGER (L) AND CHIEFTAIN (R)

A POSSIBLE GUN–ABOVE–HULL MBT LAYOUT

▶ An early British proposal, on a Centurion tank hull and running gear, for a turretless MBT mounting the gun above the hull. (MoD)

protection. This implies not only a greater degree of mobility and agility, both on roads and across country, than current and next-generation MBTs, but also some means of detecting and, if possible, engaging the inward-flying missile, so that avoiding action can be taken; there is little hope of avoiding the gun-fired projectile due to its short time of flight. The missile-detecting system should, ideally, be able to detect and destroy automatically any missile engaging the tank; this, however, implies the tank carrying another weapon system especially for this purpose, in addition to the considerable electronics package required for the detection and engagement system. Obviously such a system would be too bulky to be installed in a lightened MBT, apart from being too expensive for each tank to have one, and some other solution will be required. The most likely would appear to be the provision of one specialized anti-aircraft/anti-missile tank per MBT squadron/company, or possibly even per troop/platoon, with the specific task of detecting and engaging enemy aircraft or missiles flying into or towards the unit area. Such a vehicle could be complemented by the provision of a simple warning detector for the commander of each MBT, to give warning of the direction of impending attack when his attention is otherwise engaged, so that the vehicle can take avoiding action.

Some armies, such as those of the USSR, USA, France, Holland, Sweden and West Germany, already employ specialist AA vehicles in the armoured company, and these can readily be modified to engage missiles as well as aircraft. Their detection systems will need to be passive, as opposed to the present active radar, if they are not to be knocked out early in the battle by radar-seeking missiles.

Having dealt briefly with the detection, warning and engagement aspects of hit avoidance, let us now turn to mobility, the other component. Apart from operator competence, which is taken for granted, AFV mobility is a function of:

1. The ratio of the power available to its weight (power/weight ratio) and the speed of response of the power plant.
2. The power train.
3. The suspension's ability to absorb the inequalities of the ground surface.
4. The ability of the wheels and tracks (the running gear) to stand up to high-speed running.

As far as power outputs are concerned, present-day power plants, whether of compression ignition, internal combustion or gas turbine type, are quite adequate to give the power/weight ratios required for adequate AFV mobility; the limiting factor is the engine volume necessary to accommodate these outputs. Power/weight ratios have crept remorselessly upwards since the war when ratios of under 10bhp/tonne were common for infantry tanks and of 15–17bhp/tonne for cruiser tanks and their foreign equivalents; today, 20 and even 25bhp/tonne is common for the present generation of MBTs such as the US Abrams, the Soviet T-72 and the British Challenger. For the prediction of the performance of a main battle tank, the ratio of gross engine power to vehicle laden weight provides a

◀ **A typical modern anti-aircraft gun tank, in this case the West German Gepard, mounting twin 35mm automatic guns and search and tracking radars on the chassis of the Leopard 1 MBT. (Krauss Maffei)**

good estimate; as a yardstick, a ratio of 15–20bhp/ tonne has been considered satisfactory, 20–25bhp/ tonne good and over 25bhp/tonne excellent up until the present. For the greater agility likely to be demanded for the lighter future generation of MBT, however, a ratio in excess of 30bhp/tonne may well be essential, particularly when the power losses in the gearbox and final drives, which may each reduce the power available at the track sprockets by 15 per cent, are taken into consideration. A useful rule of thumb used by the general design team is that net power at the driving sprockets is in the region of 75 per cent of gross engine output.

Most current MBTs are powered by compression ignition (diesel) engines; the switch from petrol was made after the war, on the grounds of logistics, reduced flammability, lower cost and greater availability in the required grades, although there was a brief period in the late 1950s when it was British War Office policy for the engines of AFVs to have a multi-fuel capability. It was to meet this requirement that the disastrous L.60 opposed-piston engine for the British Chieftain MBT was developed; like most multi-purpose devices, it fulfilled none satisfactorily and was happily abandoned by the British Army in the Chieftain's successor, Challenger, for a Perkins/Rolls-Royce Condor V-12 diesel engine with an output of 1,200bhp. Current MBT power plants in NATO countries and the

USSR all have outputs in the 1,000–1,500bhp range, and all, with the notable exception of the US Abrams, which has an Avco AGT 1500 gas turbine of 1,500bhp, are compression ignition (diesel) engines of roughly comparable volume and weight. The diesel engine, making use as it does of tried and tested technology from the commercial heavy vehicle application, appeals to the conservative military user, who tends to eschew the novel and the exotic; nevertheless, the gas turbine has many attractions for the AFV user, among which are its instant full power capability from start, its excellent cold starting characteristics and the greater power produced in relation to its weight and volume than diesels. It is, however, fuel-hungry, and consumes up to twice as much fuel as a diesel engine of equivalent power; volume saved on its smaller cooling system is therefore used by the increased fuel storage required. The gas turbine is also sensitive to dust ingestion causing erosion of turbine blades, and an AFV lives in an environment that is very dusty, much of it of its own making; it also costs approximately twice as much to produce as a diesel engine of similar power, although its life-cycle costs are lower.

It is abundantly clear that present engine power outputs are quite sufficient to give the future generation of lighter, more agile tanks a more than adequate ratio of power to weight; what is now required are power plants of these outputs but of smaller volume, in order to reduce the dimensions of the newer MBTs. Research programmes to this end are currently under way in several countries, involving rotary piston stratified charge engines using the Wankel principle and adiabatic diesels in which the combustion zones are thermally insulated with ceramics, thus reducing or eliminating the need for the conventional cooling system, which can occupy a volume of 60–80 per cent of the volume of the engine itself in current diesel tank power plants. Obviously the elimination of the cooling system, or the major part of it, could produce the desired reduction in volume of the power pack. Studies continue also into ways of improving the fuel consumption of the gas turbine, as well as into alternative systems using electric drive.

Any discussion of power for AFVs must, however, inevitably revert to the basic truth that it is the power delivered to the sprockets which matters, and every consideration must be given to that part of the tank's power pack that transmits the engine's power to the tracks, that is the transmission and final drives. The advantages of a factory-matched power pack, consisting of the power plant and its cooling system together with a matched transmission, including steering system, brakes and final drives, are obvious; the complete pack can be tested, delivered and installed as one component, rather than having to instal each item separately into the vehicle and then test it, as was the former practice. By developing a complete power pack, the designer can also optimize the space available for its installation. The aim in future generations of MBT will be to increase the efficiency of the transmission with a view to reducing fuel consumption, and to reduce its volume, and weight, by improved design. Now that their initial fluid filtration and heating problems have been overcome, hydrostatic steering systems, with their infinitely variable turning radius, are likely to replace the earlier mechanical geared systems, which gave only fixed radii of turn according to speed and gear engaged.

The weight distribution of the lighter MBT of the future will be very different from that of the conventional turreted tank of today by virtue of dispensing with the central turret, of locating the ammunition stowage and the auto-loader at the rear and of redistributing the heavy frontal armour over the whole tank. Were the conventional layout of mechanical components to be followed, and the engine and transmission positioned at the rear, the tank would be uncomfortably rear-heavy, with an adverse effect on its mobility performance; to counter this, therefore, it is probable that these components would be located at the front of the vehicle, as in the Swedish 'S'-Tank and the Israeli Merkava. The forward placing of the engine and transmission would have the additional benefit of adding to the frontal protection of the vehicle and of enabling a rear crew entrance and exit to be provided, again as on the Merkava.

There is, however, irrefutable evidence that the main limitation upon the cross-country speed of an AFV is not power but ride. The crew, even if harnessed, can tolerate only a given amount of bumping and there is a limit to the robustness that can be designed into optical and electronic devices; but both the crew and the material payload of the vehicle must be capable of operating not only upon reaching their destination but also during the journey to it. The heavy tanks of the First World War, which had no form of springing, could travel across country at not more than 1mph because of vibration and crew discomfort, while, until recently, the average speed of many different types and vintages of AFV over a wide variety of terrain has been shown to be only between 7 and 11mph for the same reason. The only prospect of increasing this speed significantly lies in improved suspension design, as the other alternative, to decrease considerably the unsprung weight, always very high in AFVs, of the vehicle is impossible to achieve without lowering the performance of the vehicle in other directions.

During the inter-war years, AFVs used metal springs in either helical (coil), volute or disc form; these have the drawback that good performance demands long springs, which are not easy to accommodate in a design; the only design which successfully managed to incorporate suitably long coil springs was that of the US designer Christie, whose designs were adapted by the British in their cruiser tanks of the Second World War and by the USSR in their wartime T-34 medium tank. Although giving a good cross-country speed performance, the Christie suspension had the disadvantage of decreasing the usable internal vehicle width, as the spring units were mounted vertically inside the hull lower side plates.

During the Second World War, the Germans made extensive use of the torsion spring to suspend their Pz Kpfw III, Panther and Tiger tanks; these springs were in the form of long bars mounted laterally across and inside the belly plate, one spring to each wheel. These

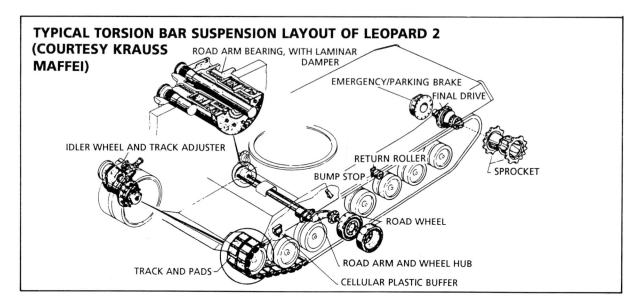

**TYPICAL TORSION BAR SUSPENSION LAYOUT OF LEOPARD 2
(COURTESY KRAUSS MAFFEI)**

ROAD ARM BEARING, WITH LAMINAR DAMPER

EMERGENCY/PARKING BRAKE

FINAL DRIVE

IDLER WHEEL AND TRACK ADJUSTER

RETURN ROLLER

BUMP STOP

SPROCKET

ROAD WHEEL

TRACK AND PADS

ROAD ARM AND WHEEL HUB

CELLULAR PLASTIC BUFFER

torsion bars performed adequately, were reliable and, unless damaged by anti-tank mines, long-lived, with the result that, since the war, this type of suspension has been used extensively by most countries in their tracked AFVs. Despite its simplicity, however, the torsion bar has many disadvantages, not the least of which is the one common to all metal springs, namely a fixed 'rate' regardless of deflection. Another serious disadvantage, particularly where efforts to decrease the height and weight of future MBTs are concerned, is the additional height, some 6–8 inches minimum, required within the hull to accommodate them; this extra volume has to be armoured, and hence adds weight which can ill be spared. Some form of damper is also required on at least the front and rear wheel stations and probably more, adding more weight, while bump stops will be needed on all wheel stations, adding still more weight. It will thus be seen that the beguiling relative cheapness and simplicity of the torsion bar on its own has hidden penalties of vehicle height and weight, as well as cost when the complete suspension system is taken into account.

Knowing these disadvantages of the metal spring, AFV suspension designers have for years been seeking to use the properties of gas as a spring, such as variable 'rate', capacity for large wheel movement and small volume, in a suspension unit incorporating its own hydraulic damper. Breakthroughs have recently been achieved by designers in Britain, USA, Japan and

France, and the British Challenger has been the first NATO MBT to enter service equipped with this type of suspension, variously known as hydro-pneumatic or hydrogas.

The advent of a reliable hydro-pneumatic suspension unit has helped to solve at a stroke two of the problems facing the design team for the future MBT, namely, how to reduce the height and weight of the vehicle while at the same time increasing the cross-country speed at which the crew and equipment begin to experience discomfort. The hydrogas units are mounted externally to the vehicle on the hull lower side plate, in the normally unused space between the top and bottom runs of the track, thus dispensing with the torsion bar's need for the false floor and additional vehicle height to accommodate it; it has the additional advantage in this position of giving extra protection to the lower hull and of not having the torsion bar's vulnerability to damage from anti-tank mines. It can be a very long and difficult job to extract and replace torsion bars damaged in this way, whereas to replace an externally-mounted hydrogas unit similarly damaged is relatively easy.

Two other canards concerning hydrogas suspension, put about by the proponents of the torsion bar, particularly in West Germany, have also been laid to rest as a result of British experience with hydrogas, namely that excessive heat would be generated in the units, leading to unreliability, and the rise and fall of the tank with ambient temperature changes would lead to track-throwing when starting from cold; neither of these gloomy prognostications has been borne out by experience. Some countries, such as the Republic of Korea in their Rokit MBT, worried by the forecasts of the torsion bar lobby concerning hydrogas, have chosen the worst of both worlds by using torsion bars on the middle wheel stations, thus incurring the height and weight penalty inherent with this system, in combination with hydrogas units on the more highly worked front and rear stations. Others, such as the US with their M-1 and the West Germans with Leopard 2 pay the same penalty by using external rotary dampers in combination with torsion bars, together with complicated hydraulic bump stops, thus adding even more unnecessary weight; to give them their due, however, both countries were frightened off hydrogas suspension by their joint experience of the very complicated systems tried on the US/FRG MBT-70 in the 1960s.

Finally we come to the other possibility, mentioned above, for increasing suspension performance, that of reducing the unsprung weight. The main components contributing to this weight are the road wheels, tyres and tracks, of which the latter account for the greatest proportion; the running gear, which consists of the tracks, wheels and suspension, of the average MBT accounts for some 22 per cent, and tracks alone for some 10 per cent of total vehicle weight. If a substantial reduction of either track or wheel/tyre weight could be achieved without loss of performance, therefore, a useful contribution to reduction of the overall vehicle weight and improvement of suspension performance would have been made. Unfortunately, however, these components are very heavily stressed during their life, which is spent in an adverse environment of extremes of temperature, dust and wet; they are also, especially the tracks, difficult to replace in the field as well as being weighty and bulky items to carry in the logistic pipeline, and they are therefore designed with life rather than weight in mind. Ideally, the tracks of a tracked AFV should have a life equal to that between base overhauls of the vehicle to which they are fitted. In fact, an average track life is 8,000–10,000 kilometres, which is the best compromise available between weight, life and cost, and unless some new material with better characteristics than, and as cheap as, steel comes along it is unlikely that unsprung weight will be radically reduced by changes in track design and manufacture.

Wheels have traditionally been made from steel forgings, and some weight saving could be made here by changing to light alloy. Light alloy wheels are, however, more expensive than steel, are more susceptible to damage and suffer from fatigue failure; because, also, of the thicker wheel sections required by light alloy, the overall weight saving resulting from the change of material is unlikely to justify the increased cost. Tyres are a constant source of trouble, due partly to the internal heating caused by the rapidly alternating compression and expansion during cross-country travel, partly to the friction with the tracks and partly to physical damage caused by stones and other objects encountered; until, however, some new material with better characteristics than rubber is discovered, and many have been tried without success, rubber will remain the preferred tyre material and there will be no scope for unsprung weight reduction there.

The general design of the future MBT of the 21st century is now clear; it is likely to be a tracked vehicle, weighing between 35–40 tonnes, with a crew of three (commander, gunner and driver), armed with a smooth-bore 105mm gun carried in an external retracting pedestal mount and carrying an auto-loader with its rear-mounted ammunition stowage. It will be equipped with laser rangefinder and passive thermal day/night sight and will have 360° traverse and the specified elevation and depression, in a mounting slaved to the commander's stabilized and gunner's sight. The armour layout will be unconventional, the main armour being around the crew pod in the hull; the top will be evenly armoured to protect against top attack, and armour will be composite and reactive, to give protection against both chemical and kinetic energy attack. The tank will be powered by either a lateral-mounted gas turbine or an advanced diesel engine, positioned at the front of the tank to give additional frontal protection to the crew and with an output high enough to give the tank a power/weight ratio of 30bhp/tonne, equivalent to an average car. Transmission will be automatic, steering hydrostatic and suspension hydro-pneumatic. The various components of such a tank will be described in detail in the following chapters.

Having established an acceptable basis for a main battle tank in the 21st century, let us now look at requirements for other types of AFV in the same time-frame. Economies of scale can be made if these can be based upon the MBT, using the hull, power train and running gear of this vehicle upon which to build other variants. There will obviously be a requirement for a recovery vehicle, capable of reaching the most remote battle tank requiring recovery and field repair, and the use of the MBT chassis as a basis ensures that the Armoured Recovery Vehicle (ARV) will have comparable mobility to its parent vehicle. By virtue of the basic MBT having a forward-mounted engine, the rear of the vehicle will be available for the carriage of the recovery crew of fitters as well as the necessary tools, welding kit and spares. The vehicle will be unarmed, except for a machine-gun for local protection and the personal weapons of the crew, although smoke-projectors will be useful for vehicle recovery under fire; night driving and vision equipment will also be needed so that the ARV crew can navigate and locate broken-down tanks in the dark. An hydraulically operated crane will also be required on the ARV for the lifting of heavy parts.

Another vehicle requiring similar mobility to the MBT, and for which the MBT chassis and running gear will make an ideal basis, is the anti-aircraft vehicle of which mention has already briefly been made. This vehicle will be required to accompany the MBT company/squadron on the march, giving AA protection and warning to the MBT column against attacking helicopters, fixed-wing aircraft and missiles. It could consist of the hull, power train and running gear of the MBT, carrying a multi-missile or gun mounting with 360° traverse and the necessary radar or other locating system to which the mount would be slaved, with spare missiles or ammunition carried in place of the MBT auto-loader.

Two other main members of the MBT family can be foreseen; an infantry carrier and a bridge-layer. It has, in the past, been customary for the infantry accompanying the armour in the battle to be carried in armoured vehicles lighter and less well protected than the MBT; these vehicles, known variously as Infantry Combat Vehicles (ICV) or Armoured Personnel Carriers (APC), are generally required to carry a section of infantry, their personal weapons, ammunition and equipment, together with a vehicle crew of driver and commander, and to accompany the MBT wherever it goes. By virtue of the fact that it has been lighter, the IFV/APC is invariably more lightly armoured than its accompanying tanks, which is bad for the morale of the infantry it is carrying apart from increasing the likelihood of its being knocked out by weapons that can not penetrate the tank. Apart, therefore, from the

greater logistic convenience of having both MBT and IFV/APC based on a common chassis and using common components, a further benefit lies in both vehicles having the same armour protection, while separate design and production facilities are not required.

At present, the British have the 62-tonne Challenger MBT and the completely different 23-tonne IFV Warrior, the Germans have the 60-tonne Leopard 2 and the completely different 28.5-tonne IFV Marder and the Americans have the 60-tonne Abrams MBT and the completely different 22.5-tonne IFV Bradley working together. Instead of basing the IFV/APC on the MBT chassis and forming part of its 'family', all three countries have preferred to build a family based upon the IFV, leaving the MBT as a unique, and therefore more expensive vehicle. It would appear more sensible to base the 'family' upon the MBT; an IFV/APC so based will have more internal room for the carriage of the infantry and their weapons and equipment without the necessity for cramping them uncomfortably, and the front-mounted engine will leave the rear of the vehicle clear to provide entry and exit for the infantrymen and their weapons. Laden, the MBT based IFV/APC will weigh approximately the same as the MBT, and will have the same power/weight ratio and the same mobility as its parent vehicle.

The other essential member of the MBT family of vehicles will be an armoured bridgelayer; it has been the practice since the Second World War to base an armoured bridgelayer on the current tank, and it is likely that this will continue. The bridge will obviously have to be capable of supporting the MBT and should separate from its carrier during the laying process so that the latter can be employed elsewhere while the bridge is in place.

The MBT family will therefore consist of:

1. The MBT.
2. The IFV/APC.
3. The AA/Anti-missile vehicle.
4. The bridgelayer.

Other variants will undoubtedly be built for special tasks, particularly in wartime, but the family as listed above should cover the essentials; other tasks for which variants might eventually be required could include mine-clearing and armoured engineer functions.

Having discussed at some length the general design aspects of the future generation of main battle tanks and variants, we will now turn to the other main function of armoured fighting vehicles in the armies of today and tomorrow, with a view to understanding the problems involved, and seeing how they have been solved in the past and how they might be solved in the 21st century. This is mobile, far-ranging reconnaissance, a function formerly carried out by the horsed cavalry until the stalemate of the First World War and the mechanization that followed it put paid to the horse in the modern army as anything other than a spare time hobby for those of its members who could still afford it.

For deep reconnaissance, a vehicle is desirable that is fast and quiet, and which has a large radius of action, some armour protection and some means of self-defence, as well as a long-range radio for communication with its base. It must be a vehicle with some cross-country ability, although it will hope to move primarily on roads and tracks when possible. Such a vehicle could, in theory, be either wheeled or tracked, although the noise signature, limited radius of action and fuel requirements of the future MBT would appear to rule it out of the running for this requirement.

The relative advantages and disadvantages of wheeled versus tracked vehicles have not yet been discussed in this chapter, and this appears to be a good point at which to do so. The first armoured vehicles to be employed by either side during the First World War were armoured cars; these were, quite literally, civilian cars which had been provided with improvised armour and a light weapon, and were used on the Western Front by the Belgian and British Armies in the early stages of the war to harry the advancing German Army and, by the British Royal Naval Air Service, to protect their Dunkirk base. Both British and French produced armoured cars on suitably reinforced civilian vehicle chassis throughout 1915, but opportunities for their use became progressively less as the war dragged on and the opposing trench systems made the country near the front lines impassable for wheeled vehicles; and here is revealed one of the main disadvantages of the wheeled as against the tracked vehicle, its limited cross-country capacity. This is due partly to the limited number of points of contact between its wheels and the ground, with consequential higher ground pressure than desirable, and partly to the ease with which the

▶
The British Austin Peerless armoured car of the First World War, one of the many early attempts to combine the mobility of the motor car with the protection offered by armour plate. (Author's collection)

tyre treads become clogged with mud in soft going; they therefore tend to present a smooth and slippery surface to the ground surface, rather than the aggressive one presented by a tank's track, with resultant wheel slip. Partly as a result of this characteristic, there is a vehicle weight above which the tracked vehicle has the advantage and below which the advantage lies with wheels. This weight is in the region of 10 tonnes. The limitation of wheeled vehicles on soft, plastic soils is one of loss of traction for the reasons given above; under other going conditions, however, wheeled vehicles can operate off the road as well as tracked vehicles, while on hard smooth going such as roads they perform rather better. They also offer enough other advantages to make them worth considering for a number of roles, particularly within the general weight limitation already mentioned, the most important of which is that of deep reconnaissance.

The other main advantages possessed by wheeled as against tracked vehicles are:

1. Capacity for high sustained road speed.
2. Low noise signature.
3. Longer range for a given quantity of fuel.
4. No damage to roads.
5. Greater reliability and longer life.

The disadvantages of wheeled AFVs include:

1. Limited hull width within overall width, due to space required by Ackermann steered wheels.
2. Limited hull width limits turret ring diameter and hence main armament calibre.
3. Less mass and stability to absorb recoil energy of main armament fired broadside to vehicle hull.
4. Vehicle weight limited by number of wheels and ground pressure.
5. Each wheel needs to be driven, making for complicated drive systems, particularly where wheels need also to be steered.
6. Loss of traction in soft ground.

There has been a long-standing controversy concerning the relative merits of tracks and wheels in most armies; in the British Army, it has almost achieved the status and unreality of a medieval disputation, with the unfortunate result that both tracked and wheeled solutions to the problem of the light reconnaissance AFV have been provided, at vast unnecessary design and development cost and with neither solution providing a completely satisfactory answer. One outcome has been that the tracked version, the CVR(T) or Scorpion, has tended to be used as a light tank, whereas the lesson of the Second World War was that there is no role in the modern battle for a light tank; it is too lightly armed and protected to fight for information, and money spent on the development of such a vehicle is, in the end, money wasted. As happened between the wars, the light tank has been used with reasonable success in the odd minor campaign such as the Falklands/Malvinas, but this success is liable to blind those whose job it is to know to the real function of Scorpion as a light reconnaissance vehicle, a function which it is singularly ill-fitted to carry out in an all-out war in Europe.

A tracked vehicle is also less suitable for employment in the internal security role in support of the civil power than a wheeled vehicle, partly for pyschological reasons and partly because it represents a step up in the application of minimum force. The internal security role is, however, one which can very well be carried out by a wheeled armoured reconnaissance vehicle; the highly successful use of Saladins and Ferrets in Malaysia, Oman and Libya in this role is testimony to the wheeled vehicle's suitability.

On balance, therefore, and bearing in mind the family of vehicles on the chassis of the future MBT, it would seem that the reconnaissance/internal security roles in the future could best be filled by a wheeled AFV. This would limit the armoured vehicle inventory to two basic types of armoured vehicle: a tracked family of vehicles on the MBT chassis and a wheeled family based on a future armoured car. The future armoured car should, as we have seen, have a weight in action not exceeding 10–15 tonnes; this weight should be spread over as many wheels as possible, to keep the ground pressure in the region of 12psi, giving the best compromise between adhesion on roads and sinkage in soft ground.

It is no part of an armoured car's role to fight for information; its weight will preclude it both from carrying armament sufficiently powerful to enable it to do so, and from being adequately protected against the enemy firepower likely to be brought to bear against it in combat. Armament, therefore, need be sufficient only to enable it to cover its retreat when discovered, and its protection thick enough only to protect the crew from smallarms fire, artillery shell fragments and the miscellaneous missiles likely to be encountered in riot control and internal security patrols.

The main general design criterion will be mobility, and the emphasis within mobility will be upon operating range, speed, manoeuvrability and acceleration; power/weight ratio will therefore need to be in the 25–30bhp/tonne region which, for a vehicle weight of 10–15 tonnes, will require a power plant giving an output of 300–450bhp. Many well-tried diesel engines with this output already exist; it is unlikely that there will be any startling innovations in design by the year 2000, although the adiabatic diesel engine, with its reduced cooling requirements and greater fuel economy, might well be available by then. The transmission should have a high-speed reverse gear, to enable the vehicle to reverse quickly out of trouble, and all wheels should be driven; the most suitable wheel arrangement is likely to be 6×6 or 8×8, all wheels mounting tyres that can be run at high speed for at least 50 miles when deflated ('run-flat' tyres). To enable the maximum benefit to be derived from the very high power/weight ratio, and high cross-country speeds to be maintainable, suspension will not only have to be independent for each wheel but the vertical wheel movement which it will permit will have to be quite exceptionally high; this is to ensure that the suspension can absorb the unevenness of the ground without transmitting unacceptable shocks to the crew and vehicle components. In order to achieve the required wheel movement together with the right spring characteristics, the suspension units will most probably be hydro-pneumatic.

Armament for the armoured reconnaissance vehicle, together with the necessary sighting and control system, will need to be as light and as simple as possible in order to keep the overall vehicle weight down; it is suggested that it be mounted in a light turret, traversable through 360° by means of a simple power system which, for lightness, is likely to be an all-electric one. For local protection, the turret is likely to mount a heavy calibre machine-gun and, for heavier targets when required, an anti-tank missile-launcher carrying two to four missiles. An alternative main armament might be a soft recoil 90mm or 105mm gun, with coaxial machine-gun, but such a weapons fit would require a more robust turret, a more complicated traverse system to give the necessary accuracy and probably also powered elevation of the gun; a turret so equipped is likely to raise the weight of the vehicle to an unacceptable level. Multiple smoke-grenade launchers, capable in peacetime of launching tear-gas grenades for riot control, will also be required

on the turret. Alternative turrets, interchangeable with the standard one of the basic vehicle, will probably be required for special roles; for example, mounting battlefield surveillance radar, night observation equipment, AAMGs or missiles and other reconnaissance aids.

Other versions of the basic vehicle might be required as command vehicles, personnel carriers, recovery vehicles and armoured ambulances, to name the more important members of the family; these variants would use the basic hull, chassis power plant and running gear of the armoured car, reconfigured so as to give an armoured box body in place of the turret for command personnel, infantry, recovery personnel or wounded and medical orderlies.

The operating crew of the future armoured car will, as with the future MBT, probably consist of three men: the commander, the driver and the gunner/radio operator. In other roles the number of crewmen will vary according to the task; as an infantry carrier, for example, the basic vehicle crew will probably consist of only two men, the commander and the driver, the infantry section or half-section, depending upon the size of the vehicle, being carried as passengers rather than as crew.

From this discussion, we have seen that, far from having reached the end of the road as some pundits would have us believe, the tank and other fighting vehicles have come to a branching of the way, a change of course, the road ahead being blocked. The blockage is a combination of many factors, including:

1. The new anti-tank weapons, and new directions of attack, particularly from above.
2. The weight and cost of a main battle tank with sufficient protection to withstand these new means of attack.
3. The increasingly poor strategic mobility of heavier and bigger MBTs.
4. The physical impossibility of armouring a vehicle effectively against new methods and directions of attack.

The protection of an armoured fighting vehicle has always consisted of a combination of protective armour and mobility. The inability of even the new composite and reactive armours to keep out all types and sizes of attack means that less reliance must be placed on the armour component and more on the

◀
A modern equivalent of the Peerless, in this case the 8-wheeled West German Panzer-spähwagen 'Luchs' (Lynx). This vehicle is a logical development of the highly successful wartime series of German 8-wheeled armoured cars. (Daimler Benz AG)

mobility component of protection. This in turn means smaller, more agile vehicles, able to take hit avoidance action.

Luckily, smaller vehicles are also cheaper than the present monsters; most countries are finding that the MBTs, and indeed other AFVs, of today cost too much per copy. Limitations on the size of defence budgets world-wide mean that not enough tanks can be procured to carry out all the tasks allocated to defence staffs; by producing cheaper, smaller MBTs, more tanks can be acquired for the same outlay, thus enabling defence staffs to fulfil their allotted roles more satisfactorily.

Two further benefits accrue from adopting the smaller MBT: first, by reducing the crew from four men to three, manpower and training requirements are reduced, enabling the manpower thus released to be redeployed either into other arms or services or into additional armoured regiments; secondly, the smaller tank is very much more strategically mobile than the present generation, making its transport from one theatre of operations or front to another very much easier; for a given tonnage of shipping or rail flat cars, more MBTs can be carried, while for a given number of MBTs to be transported, fewer ships, rail flats or tank transporters will be needed.

By using the MBT hull, chassis and running gear as a basis for the MICV, ARV, APC and bridgelayer, economies of scale will be possible in the production of MBT components and assemblies, even if the vehicle configurations are different from the MBT, thus further cheapening the equipment acquisition process. Similarly with the armoured car family; the use of common components and assemblies for all members of the vehicle family, regardless of role and configuration, will greatly reduce the overall cost of the family. With just two basic armoured fighting vehicles, one tracked and one wheeled, the equipment procurement process will be quicker and less costly; training of vehicle crews and repair staff will be simplified and cheapened and the logistic chain will also be simplified. The tank as a military virility symbol, where bigger means better, is dead; the smart army of the future will put its money on mobility rather than protection as a means of enabling its AFV crews to live to fight another day.

There will still be those who argue for an end to the expensive, heavy and unwieldy tank, preferring to put their money on helicopters for offensive action in support of the infantry, who should also be heli-borne, and, to a certain extent, for reconnaissance also, with the armoured car's reconnaissance role taken over, perhaps, by small air-cushion vehicles with a two-man crew. The trouble with this solution is that helicopters are more expensive, more fragile and vulnerable, noisier and, in flat, dusty conditions, very much more easily spotted. They have a fair radar cross-section and can be easily picked up by ground-based radar when not engaged in 'nap of the earth' flying. They are fairly slow-flying compared to fixed-wing combat aircraft and can easily be engaged by ground-based guns and missiles. The numbers required, and the number of aircrew to be trained to operate them, are very large, and the cost would be extremely high; they could not be relied upon to operate with any success except under conditions of complete air superiority. The main drawback to the air-cushion vehicle is its lack of manoeuvrability; lacking contact with the ground, it has no means of stopping or changing direction suddenly. It is also very noisy and has a poor payload capacity; hence it has a short range due to its inability to carry much fuel, and it can carry little if any protection for the crew. It has, however, good mobility across country and across smooth water, and can make the transition from land to water with ease; it is especially useful under marshy conditions, where the going is impassable for wheeled and tracked vehicles. Various attempts have been made, with little success, to provide the air-cushion vehicle with retractable skids or wheels with a view to improving its manoeuvrability; in theory, when a turn or a sudden stop is required, the landing gear is lowered to make contact with the ground; such aids are, however, complicated, fragile and add weight, so that one tends to get the worst of both worlds.

There seems, therefore, little likelihood of the tank being superseded on the battlefield in the foreseeable future, although the great powers have at present only the experience of the last war, and knowledge of their potential enemies' equipment, upon which to base their requirements for fighting the next one. It could well be that the armoured vehicle will be unable to survive on a nuclear battlefield, or on one in which the full spectrum of electronic warfare and anti-armour weapons is deployed, in which case it will be too late to re-equip with something better and more effective. The winners of that war, if there are any, will then know how to re-equip their armies for the next one!

Since the main body of the text was completed, there have been some further developments in the 'Main Battle Tank' category. These are listed below in alphabetical order of country responsible for design and manufacture.

Israel's Merkava Mark 3 In May 1989, Israel introduced the Merkava Mark 3. This tank, while closely resembling the Mark 2 in external appearance, differs from it in the following particulars.

Weight in action: 61 tonnes
Main armament: 120mm smooth-bore
Traverse, elevation and stabilization: all-electric
Suspension: independent coil spring per road wheel with hydraulic rotary dampers on 8 out of 12 wheel stations
Protection: (i) threat warning system on turret, (ii) modular reactive and 'special' armour
Power plant: Teledyne Continental AVDS-1790-9AR air-cooled diesel.

Great Britain's Challenger 2/2 The Challenger 2/2 is the Vickers Defence Systems' proposal for the replacement of the 600 or so Chieftains in the British tank fleet. It is basically a Challenger 2 (by which name it is still known in the British MoD), upgraded to meet the requirements of MoD Staff Requirement SR(L)4026. The MoD has funded Vickers Defence Systems for 21 months in order that they may have the opportunity to demonstrate that Challenger 2/2 can meet the British Army's Staff Requirement. Vickers have also been given responsibility for the development of an improved nature of ammunition, known as CHARM 3, to be fired from the CHARM gun already under development for the Chieftain replacement and Challenger 1.

It is intended that the demonstration phase, in which Challenger 2 will be demonstrated in competition with modified German Leopard 2 and US M-1 Abrams, will be completed by September 1990, by which time nine prototype Challenger 2 tanks and two additional turrets will have been built. In December 1990, the three tanks will be evaluated by MoD against the Staff Requirement, as a result of which the tank finally selected to replace Chieftain should enter service in the early 1990s. It will be more reliable, better protected, have greater firepower and be easier to fight and maintain than any tank in service anywhere, as of September 1989.

BIBLIOGRAPHY

Chamberlain, Peter, and Ellis, Chris. *British and American Tanks of the Second World War*. Arco Pub. Co. Inc., New York, 1969
— *British and German Tanks of the First World War*. Arms & Armour Press, 1969
Crow, Duncan, and Icks, Robert J. *Encyclopedia of Tanks*. Chartwell Books Inc., New Jersey, 1975
Foss, Christopher F. (ed.). *Jane's Armour and Artillery*. Jane's Pub. Co. Ltd., London, annually
Perkins, Major-General Ken. (ed.) *Weapons and Warfare*. Brassey's Defence Publishers, 1987

Perret, Bryan. *Soviet Armour Since 1945*. Blandford Press, 1987
Zaloga, Steven J., and Loop, James W. *Soviet Tanks and Combat Vehicles, 1946 to the Present*. Arms & Armour Press, 1987
US Government. 'Soviet Military Power – An Assessment of the Threat, 1988'. US Government Printing Office, Washington, DC, 1988

▼ A Challenger of The Royal Hussars (Prince of Wales's Own). (HQ I (Br.) Corps)